The Squirrels of Canada

Published by the National Museums
of Canada

Editor
Bonnie Livingstone
Production
Barry Boucher
Don Matheson
Design
Gregory Gregory Limited
Typesetting
Nancy Poirier Typesetting Ltd.
Printing
Bryant Press Ltd.

The Squirrels of Canada

National Museum of Natural Sciences
National Museums of Canada

S.E. Woods, Jr.

National Museum of Natural Sciences
National Museums of Canada
Ottawa, Canada K1A 0M8

Catalogue No. NM92-72/1980E
Printed in Canada
ISBN 0-660-10344-3

Édition française
Les écureuils du Canada
ISBN 0-660-90258-3

For my daughters
Victoria, Julia, and Penelope

Contents

This book could not have been written without the advice and assistance of many people.

I found the staff of the Mammalogy Branch of the National Museum of Natural Sciences particularly helpful, especially David Campbell, who showed me hundreds of skins; Dr. David Gray, who volunteered sound advice on the marmot chapters; and Dr. C.G. van Zyll de Jong, Curator of Mammals, who gave me unlimited access to his comprehensive bibliography on the Sciuridae. Dr. van Zyll de Jong was also one of the people saddled with the task of reviewing my manuscript, a chore that he performed with unfailing good humour.

At the outset of this project, I was given much needed encouragement by Mrs. Dorcas MacClintock, author of the definitive book *Squirrels of North America.* Among other important contributors in the ensuing months were: Mr. Fred Bruemmer, naturalist, author, and photographer, Montreal; Mr. Craig Campbell, environmental consultant, Waterloo; Professor Cy Hampson, naturalist, author, and photographer, Vancouver; Dr. Douglas Heard, Yellowknife, who permitted me to study his unpublished thesis on the Vancouver Island marmot; Dr. Keith Kivett, zoologist, University of Alberta; and Dr. André Steiner of Edmonton, a recognized authority on ground-squirrel behaviour.

While researching the species, I kept an eye out for Canadian sources, and found the writings of the following to be of special value: Dr. Jean Ferron, Dr. Brooker Klugh, Dr. Hoyes Lloyd, Dr. Don Meredith, Drs. Gail and Daniel Michener, and Dr. P.A. Taverner. There were also many good articles in Canadian periodicals, including: *Canadian Audubon, Canadian Field-Naturalist, Le Naturaliste canadien, Nature Canada,* and the *Victoria Field Naturalist.*

Because nearly four hundred published sources were used in the preparation of the book, the task of retrieving information would have been formidable, had not Ms. Tina Mattisen, Head of Reader Services, National Museums Library, and her assistant, Ms. Lorna Kibbee, worked so efficiently and cheerfully on my behalf.

Acknowledge-ments

I must also thank Mrs. Heather Shannon, Executive Assistant to the Director of the National Museum of Natural Sciences, for smoothing my path in countless ways.

The line drawings, which add much to the appeal and clarity of the book, were executed by Dwayne Harty, a young artist from Regina, Saskatchewan. Mr. Harty's drawings compliment the text, and reflect his deep affection for his subjects. The jacket painting was done by Jan Sharkey Thomas, an internationally acclaimed artist who lives in Manotick, Ontario. Mrs. Thomas very kindly postponed an important assignment to produce this work. The range maps were plotted by the staff of the Mammalogy Branch, National Museum of Natural Sciences, Ottawa.

Finally, I wish to thank Charles J. Mackenzie of Ottawa, who provided scholarly advice on the translation of scientific names, and Mrs. Bonnie Livingstone, Publishing Division, National Museums of Canada, who edited my manuscript.

A surprising aspect in the assembly of this book was revealed by my quest for colour photographs to illustrate the species. Most of the slides submitted were so outstanding that in many instances I was faced with a perplexing decision as to which one to use! To all who offered pictures I extend my sincere thanks. The credits for those printed are:
D. Anderson (Townsend's chipmunk); B. Theresa Aniskowicz (American red squirrel, eastern chipmunk, and woodchuck); A. Grass (Douglas' squirrel); Cy Hampson (Arctic ground squirrel, Franklin's ground squirrel, and northern flying squirrel); Douglas Heard (Vancouver Island marmot); Keith Kivett (thirteen-lined ground squirrel); Stephen Krasemann (black-tailed prairie dog and fox squirrel); Valerie May (yellow-bellied marmot and yellow-pine chipmunk); R.D. Muir, Parks Canada (hoary marmot); National Film Board, Photothèque (southern flying squirrel); Parks Canada (Columbian ground squirrel); Gary W. Seib, National Collection of Nature Photographs, National Museums of Canada (Richardson's ground squirrel); and Bryan Shantz, Western Wildlife Photos Limited (golden-mantled ground squirrel, grey or black squirrel, least chipmunk, and red-tailed chipmunk)

Squirrels are among those wild animals with which we are most familiar. We come in contact with them in the parks of many cities, in the woods and around picnic tables; and who has not seen a woodchuck in the fields, standing at the edge of its burrow? But do we realize that woodchucks belong to the squirrel family together with many related species? In fact, we do not know much about these friendly beasts unless we make a special study of them.

This book is for everyone who is curious about squirrels. It has been written by Shirley Woods, an outdoorsman and a keen observer of wildlife and nature. I am very pleased that he offered to produce it for the National Museum of Natural Sciences, as I am sure that *The Squirrels of Canada* will delight the reader, as well as inform him. The drawings are by Dwayne Harty, a young Canadian artist, and the cover is by the well-known Jan Sharkey Thomas.

Louis Lemieux
Director
National Museum
of Natural Sciences

Foreword

Having wanted to write about the squirrel family for some years, I was delighted and honoured when Dr. Louis Lemieux commissioned this book on behalf of the National Museums of Canada.

All of us can conjure up an image in our mind's eye of at least one of the Sciuridae, whether it be a woodchuck nibbling on clover, a squirrel perched above the pavement, a "gopher" gazing across the prairie, a marmot peeking from the rocks, or a chipmunk made bold by a handful of sunflower seeds. Yet many of us have only a sketchy knowledge of the various species, and there are a number of confusing myths in circulation.

The aim of this book is to present a factual account of each animal in layman's terms. In this connection, it may be fortunate that I have had no formal training in mammalogy, only a long exposure to the outdoors. As a layman, I know the difficulties of reading highly technical papers. My task, in the main, has been to gather and distill existing data.

To this end, I have been helped in my research by some of Canada's top mammalogists. These people took time from their demanding schedules to participate in a "popular" publication because they believe, as I do, that the more we know about our wildlife, the better we can appreciate it.

At my elbow were several basic texts, which I recommend to anyone interested in the squirrel family. They are: *The Mammals of Canada* by A.W.F. Banfield; *The Mammals of Alberta* by J. Dewey Soper; *The Mammals of Manitoba*, also by Dr. Soper; *The Mammals of British Columbia* by I. McTaggart Cowan and C.J. Guiguet, and *Squirrels of North America* by Dorcas MacClintock.

Preparing the manuscript has been an enlightening experience. The contents are factual, and I have tried to treat each species objectively. The recurring observation—that many members of the squirrel family are adversely affected by Man—is sad, but true.

I hope you will enjoy this book, and that it may contribute to your understanding of these attractive creatures.

S.E.W.

Preface

J. Sharkey Thomas

Ground Dweller
Forepaw
Woodchuck

Tree Dweller
Forepaw
American Red Squirrel

Squirrels (Sciuridae) are members of the largest mammalian order, Rodentia, which includes nearly one-third of the mammals in Canada. The Sciuridae are a broadly based family, comprising such diverse species as the woodchuck, the black-tailed prairie dog, a variety of chipmunks, and two flying squirrels.

Because of differences in habitat, behaviour, and appearance, the Sciuridae can be divided into two main groups: ground dwellers and tree dwellers.

Ground dwellers, who tend to hibernate in cold weather, have straight claws designed for digging burrows, while tree dwellers remain active year-round, and have curved claws to aid them in climbing. The stout and stolid woodchuck is a typical ground dweller; the slender and nervous red squirrel is a typical tree dweller.

Both groups are capable of swimming because they walk on all fours. When they enter the water, their normal movements keep them afloat, unlike the Primates (including Man), who walk upright, and must learn to swim. All the species in Canada are diurnal except the flying squirrels, which are nocturnal.

Members of the Sciuridae have prominent front teeth, a short bald muzzle, large eyes, and erect ears set in a well-rounded skull. Their dense coats terminate in bushy tails that they twitch frequently. In addition, their front paws have four fingers and an undeveloped thumb, while their hind feet have five toes.

The Sciuridae

Masseter Muscle

Squirrel Incisor

Comparison of Skulls
Rodent
Grey or Black Squirrel

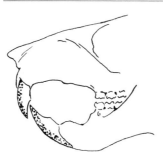

Carnivore
Raccoon

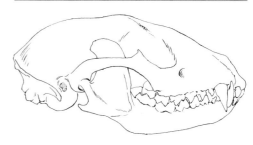

Because some of these features are shared by other mammals, zoologists use the muscle arrangement on the rodent's jaw as a means of classification. In the case of the Sciuridae, the masseter muscle is attached to the exterior surface of the skull, and runs along the zygomatic arch. Humans also have a masseter muscle, which you can feel as a hard lump at the corner of your jaw when you clench your teeth.

Another important characteristic of the squirrel family is the arrangement of their teeth. Because they are omnivores, Nature has equipped them with teeth that can cope with a wide variety of food-stuffs as well as an articulated lower jaw, which permits them to chew in a side-ways motion, the same way a cow chews its cud. Squirrels have two chisel-shaped incisors in the upper jaw (premaxillae), and a matching pair in the lower jaw (mandible). These sharp-edged buckteeth have hard enamel on the outside or front surface, and softer tissue on the inside: a combination that leads to uneven wear.

Unlike the teeth of many mammals, including adult humans, the incisors of rodents have open roots so that tooth growth is continuous, similar to that of a fingernail. Normally, the incisors stay at optimum length, because everyday wear compensates for the new growth. How-ever, if an incisor is broken, the opposite tooth will continue to grow unchecked and may eventually obstruct the squirrel's bite, or even curve back into its skull and kill it. The result of abnormal tooth-growth is known as malocclusion; pic-tured below, from the National Museums of Canada collection, is a typical example.

Malocclusion
Woodchuck skull — upper jaw

All rodents, including the Sciuridae, lack canine teeth. Instead, they have a broad gap (diastema) between their front incisors and rear grinders. This gap serves a useful purpose because it provides space for a gnawing squirrel to draw the hairy skin surrounding its lips into its mouth. The folds of skin act as a barrier, preventing debris from entering the animal's throat.

Most of the squirrels in this book are native to Canada; some can be traced back for more than twenty million years. At least one species is represented in every province and territory from New-foundland to Vancouver Island, from the Arctic to the United States border.

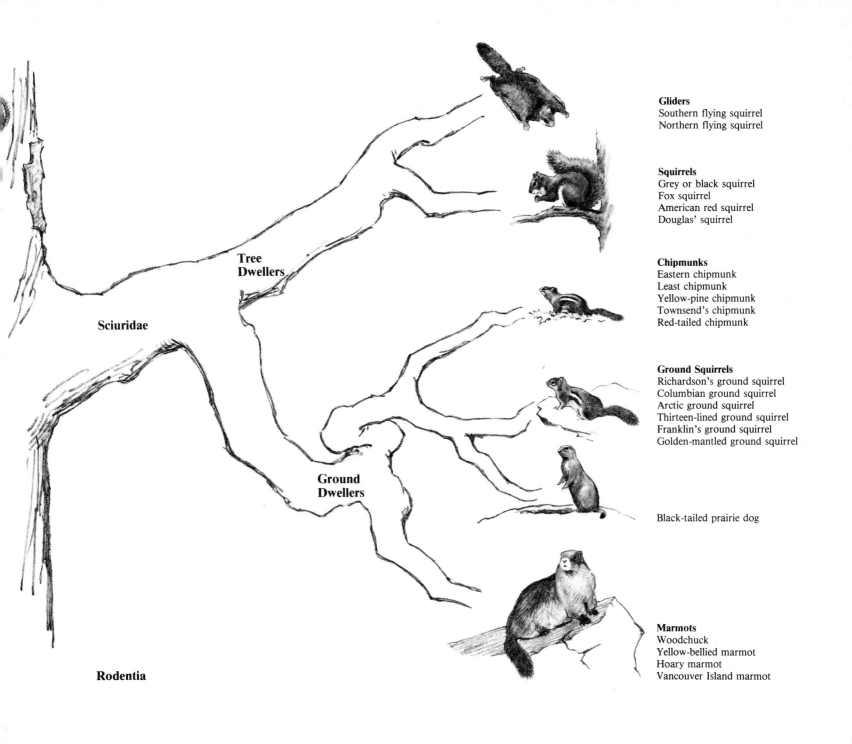

Gliders
Southern flying squirrel
Northern flying squirrel

Squirrels
Grey or black squirrel
Fox squirrel
American red squirrel
Douglas' squirrel

Chipmunks
Eastern chipmunk
Least chipmunk
Yellow-pine chipmunk
Townsend's chipmunk
Red-tailed chipmunk

Ground Squirrels
Richardson's ground squirrel
Columbian ground squirrel
Arctic ground squirrel
Thirteen-lined ground squirrel
Franklin's ground squirrel
Golden-mantled ground squirrel

Black-tailed prairie dog

Marmots
Woodchuck
Yellow-bellied marmot
Hoary marmot
Vancouver Island marmot

Tree Dwellers

Sciuridae

Ground Dwellers

Rodentia

Woodchuck
Marmotte commune
Marmota monax

Common Names

The woodchuck is frequently called a groundhog. Other names are chuck, marmot, and whistle pig; the last name is attributable to his high-pitched call. In French Canada, the early voyageurs referred to the woodchuck as *le siffleur* "the whistler", a term they also applied to the Common Goldeneye because of the whistling sound of its wings in flight. Ernest Thompson Seton, one of Canada's great naturalists, liked to call him the "Red Monk" in recognition of his colour and solitary habits.

This mammal's scientific name, *Marmota monax*, is derived from two Latin words: *Marmota* meaning "marmot", and *monax* meaning "solitary".

Description

The woodchuck is thick-bodied, with a short neck. From a distance he appears grey-brown and may be mistaken at first glance for a stump or broken post protruding from the grass. Being the third largest of our Sciuridae, after the hoary and yellow-bellied marmots, he can weigh up to 6 kg and attain an overall length of 65 cm. Normally, an adult woodchuck weighs around 3 kg, and is 50 to 55 cm long.

This rodent has prominent white teeth, a blunt grizzled muzzle, black eyes, and short ears. His body is a warm brown, while his feet, claws, and stubby tail are black. This is only a general description because the colour of a woodchuck is highly variable, and his pelt contains many shades from pale buff to black. Abnormal colouring is common in this species; there are frequent sightings of albino, melanistic, and russet animals. The woodchuck's coat is multi-hued, with coarse guard hairs and rather fine underfur.

Woodchuck

Canadian Range

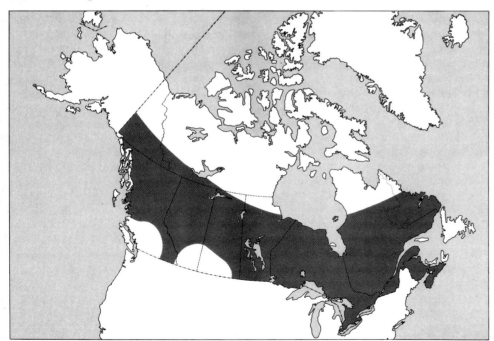

Range

The woodchuck is found all across mainland Canada, from Labrador to the Yukon, but is not present on Anticosti Island, in Prince Edward Island, Cape Breton, or Newfoundland. It is not certain why he is absent from these islands, because sections of each appear to have ideal habitat; possibly the sea has acted as a barrier.

The number of woodchucks varies with the terrain; some areas are barren, while others support as many as two animals to the hectare.

Behaviour

The woodchuck is independent, curious, and may not seem very bright. He is well known for his sharp whistle, which he normally uses as a danger signal. Woodchucks are peaceful by nature, but will not hesitate to threaten intruders (or their own kind), by gnashing their teeth and chattering fiercely. When cornered, they will fight to the death.

This marmot is not built for speed, and is further handicapped by being flat-footed (plantigrade). At full gallop, approximately 16 km/h, he shuffles along like a fur-covered bowl of jelly.

The woodchuck can swim and, despite his plump physique, is a surprisingly good climber. Dr. C.G. van Zyll de Jong, Curator of Mammals at the National Museum of Natural Sciences, Ottawa, wrote me a note concerning a woodchuck he saw on a spring walk behind his house.

I discovered the woodchuck about four metres up in a young elm. The field was flooded in low spots and it is conceivable that the wet conditions induced this animal to climb the tree on my approach.

Groundhog Day is part of North American folklore. The legend says that if a woodchuck emerges from his hole on February second and sees his shadow, he returns to his burrow and there will be six more weeks of winter; if the day is dark and overcast and there are no shadows, then spring will come early. While there is absolutely no scientific evidence to support this belief, it gives the chuck some harmless publicity once a year.

Personality

More than fifty years ago, Ernest Thompson Seton made this observation on the woodchuck in his *Lives of Game Animals*:

The warm, bright days with greening grass come on, the cold and the snow are gone. The Woodchuck sits at the door of his cell, enjoying to the full the good things of life. . . . Well fed, unafraid, revelling in the warm sun, stretched prone, or rearing back against a bank, his limp limbs drooped in sensuous sloth, he rejoices in the spring wine of the air and yields . . . to the subtle, vital thrill which stirs the hidden springs of song.

Habitat

The woodchuck likes well-drained open land with occasional ridges and gravel banks. During the summer, when he is feeding heavily (and prefers to be close to his work), pastures, meadows, and fields are his favourite spots. With the onset of cold weather, and the slowing of his metabolism, he retires to a more sheltered, brushy area to hibernate.

An industrious and discriminating homemaker, the woodchuck sites his burrow with care, and may displace more than a quarter tonne of earth while digging it. Normally he lives alone and occupies at least two dens during the course of a year.

His summer residence is located in a lush feeding area, such as a meadow or field, while his winter den is usually at the edge of a forest (the roots at the base of a tree are a favourite spot) or a fenceline. Both summer and winter quarters are similar in that they have an obvious front entrance, a cunningly concealed bolt hole, a sleeping chamber lined with grass, and a spoil room, where faeces are deposited.

The woodchuck usually sites his den on a ridge or slope because this sort of location has natural drainage and sufficient elevation for him to observe the surrounding countryside.

The completed burrow has a sleeping chamber approximately 40 cm in diameter, which provides just room enough for the animal to curl up in a ball. Connected by a tunnel is the spoil room. Some of the excavated earth is left in the spoil room to cover the faeces, but most is deposited outside where a significant amount is used to make a platform at the main entrance. The bolt hole is used to spy from, and to escape through; the chute permits him to drop from sight. Such concealed exits are valued by humans as well; Sir John A. Macdonald had a "bolt hole" in the form of a secret door leading out of his office in the Parliament Buildings.

Occasionally, a woodchuck will make an elaborate den with as many as five entrances, and up to 12 m of tunnel. This is unusual; a more typical burrow is the one illustrated.

A Main entrance
B Hidden entrance
C Main passage
D Nest
E Alternate nest

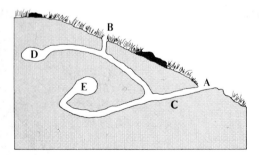

Feeding Habits

The woodchuck is primarily herbivorous and normally feeds during daylight. However, early in the spring, when food is scarce, he may forage after dusk, and he will occasionally include animal matter in his diet such as the young of ground-nesting birds, or large insects like June bugs. Although some gardeners consider the woodchuck to be an indiscriminate glutton, his favourite plants are clover, alfalfa, and dandelion.

The chuck has an enormous appetite, and can eat more than 0.5 kg of vegetation in 12 hours. This is understandable, because hibernation may produce a 40 per cent loss in body weight, which the animal must replace during the summer if he is to survive the coming winter.

Feeding usually takes place within 100 m of his den. In July, fat begins to accumulate on the lower stomach, then the hindquarters, and finally on the back and shoulders. Maximum weight is attained in September, just prior to hibernation.

Life Cycle

Woodchucks mate in March or April, depending upon the latitude. The period of gestation is approximately 31 days, and the litter ranges from 2 to 8 pups, with the average being 4.

The young are born hairless and blind, weighing approximately 28 g. During the next month they grow rapidly, doubling their length and increasing their weight fivefold. They are weaned at six weeks; by this time they have grown a full but sombre coat, and look like miniature adults.

Normally dispersal of the young takes place in the third month, although some spend the first winter with their mother. When the little ones disperse, they usually journey a very short distance (within sight of the home den) before digging a shallow burrow of their own. Woodchucks attain full growth in their second year.

Adult animals commence their annual moult in May, with new fur growing in at the tail, and progressing forward to the head. Young woodchucks are often late starting their moult and sometimes their new coat is incomplete at the start of winter. Both the young and adults put on fat in the late summer, and enter hibernation in September and October.

Many woodchucks hibernate in or near their summer burrows; others leave their open-country feeding dens around the end of September, and move to a more-sheltered location. Regardless of the site, the hibernating procedure is the same. They seal themselves into the sleeping chamber with a soil plug, and then curl up with their head between their hind feet. Over a period of days they gradually slip into a profound slumber.

The deep sleep of hibernation causes dramatic changes in their metabolism; body temperature falls from a normal 38°C to a low of 8°C to 17°C; heartbeat slows from 80 beats to 4 or 5 per minute; and respiration declines from around 40 breaths per minute to as few as one breath every 5 minutes.

Most authorities agree that the process of waking takes a matter of hours, and that the woodchuck's torpor is interrupted periodically, every 2 to 20 days. Old males are the first to go into hibernation, and the first to become active in the spring.

Natural Enemies

Before the encroachment of civilization, the woodchuck was preyed upon by the wolf, bear, cougar, coyote, and fox. Now, in most of his range, the only predators left are the coyote, fox, and domestic dog. However, young chucks are still vulnerable to a number of other predators, including hawks and snakes. Disease is not a significant factor in woodchuck mortality, possibly because of his solitary existence and a high level of personal cleanliness. Unlike many other mammals, the woodchuck is not seriously affected by external parasites, nor by the penetrating larvae of the botfly (*Cuterebra*). Barring human interference, a reasonable life expectancy for this species is 6 years.

Relations with Humans

Paradoxically, humans are the woodchuck's worst enemy as well as the cause of its "population explosion" over the past century. As we cleared the forests, we accidentally improved the habitat for *Marmota monax*, and destroyed it for the animals that preyed on him. Despite systematic and often brutal efforts to reduce his numbers, the woodchuck is probably more widespread today than before the country was settled.

The woodchuck's appetite for greens, and his burrowing habits, have lost him many friends in the farming world, as this letter written at the turn of the century will attest:

I have looked in vain for some one redeeming trait in this sneaking, grovelling curse to the agriculture of our State. He is a gross feeder, devouring nearly as much clover as a full-grown Sheep; he eats to give him strength to dig holes, and then digs holes to give him an appetite for more clover. He takes supreme delight in tearing the bark from young fruit trees, and will wipe out entirely a good sized bean patch in a day. (Seton 1929:309).

In the woodchuck's defence, it should be added that these same holes provide homes for other more welcome, and more valuable, animals such as foxes, rabbits, raccoons, and skunks. During the annual spring burning of the fields, chuck holes save the lives of many species, including young game birds. Particular mention must be made of the fox who is both an ally of the farmer and a valuable furbearer. The much-maligned woodchuck not only provides the fox with lodging, but is a staple item in his diet.

Since groundhog shooting has become the pastime of a substantial number of hunters, the woodchuck has a recreational value, and may take some of the hunting pressure off larger and scarcer mammals such as deer and moose. His flesh is quite palatable when properly prepared, but special care must be taken to remove the pungent anal glands before cooking! The pelt of the woodchuck is unsuitable for garments because of the wayward guard hairs and wispy underfur, and has no commercial value.

The study of the woodchuck has contributed to medical knowledge, particularly to such operating procedures as open-heart surgery that require a lowering of body temperature with a corresponding reduction in respiration and heart rate.

Where to Observe
The woodchuck is one of the easiest animals to observe. All you need do is to take a drive to the outskirts of town on a summer evening and you can spot him in the open fields. I see as many as a dozen on the way to my home from the Ottawa airport; all are within the city limits.

Yellow-bellied Marmot
Marmotte à ventre jaune
Marmota flaviventris

Common Names

The yellow-bellied marmot is often called a rockchuck: a fitting nickname because this rodent resembles a wood-chuck, and dwells among rocks. He has also been called yellow groundhog, yellow belly, and yellow whistler; the last name was applied because, like all marmots, he employs a high-pitched whistle to communicate.

His scientific name, *Marmota flaviventris*, is a direct Latin translation: *Marmota* (marmot) *flavi* (yellow) *ventris* (belly).

Description

The yellow-bellied marmot is shaped like a woodchuck, but he is larger, and has different markings. From a distance, his most noticeable features are the golden shade of his coat, and the yellow fur on his belly. Distinguishing marks visible at closer range are: a dark head with a pale band across the muzzle, yellow patches on each side of his neck, buff-coloured paws, and a short brown tail. This, like all other descriptions, can only cover typical features since melanistic and albino animals are not uncommon.

As with other marmots, a yellow-bellied marmot's size varies with sex and age. An adult male, weighing as much as 4.5 kg, and measuring 70 cm from nose to tip of tail, is considered as average as a yearling female weighing only 2 kg and measuring 45 cm overall.

Yellow-bellied Marmot

Canadian Range

Range

Like Lord Selkirk's Scottish crofters, who settled in the Red River Valley, yellow-bellied marmots are also highlanders living in the West. These animals are found in the central Rocky Mountains of southern Alberta and British Columbia, at altitudes of 700 to 3500 m above sea level. Although they live in widely spaced colonies, they are gregarious, and a single colony may host up to 25 marmots per hectare.

Behaviour

Yellow-bellied marmots live in a patriarchal society where the males are polygamous. This means that an adult male in a colony will have a harem of several females, each of whom may provide him with offspring. Occasionally, an old patriarch will have a many as six or seven females in his harem. Because of this social system, most colonies have a preponderance of adult females, as well as yearlings of both sexes. Agonistic behaviour is constant in the life of a marmot colony, and studies indicate that some of the most aggressive and dominant members are mature females. Losers in agonistic encounters are faced with three alternatives: to submit and become a subordinate in the family; to submit and retire to a den on the outskirts of the colony; or to leave the colony altogether. The extent of the winner's hostility determines the loser's fate. For instance, an old male will probably banish a young male from the colony because the juvenile will mature and become a more serious threat, whereas a dominant female may be satisfied as long as her adversary stays out of her territory.

Many of the rockchucks who leave the colony are killed by predators; of those who survive, some join another colony, while a few may establish a colony of their own.

Although agonistic behaviour among marmots may appear to be a self-destructive process, it is actually a major reason for the survival of the species. The forced dispersal of young animals, particularly surplus males, not only prevents inbreeding, but also ensures that the population of the colony will not exceed the grazing capacity of the surrounding terrain.

Yellow-bellied marmots are most active during the early morning and late afternoon; the interim hours are spent in their dens, or sunbathing on a nearby rock. On a fine day, they act like vacationers on a Florida beach; at first they lie broadside to the sun, for maximum exposure, and then as its rays become more intense, they change position so they receive its warmth obliquely. Despite their relaxed manner and chunky bodies, they are extremely agile and can negotiate a narrow ledge or sheer rock face with ease. It is fortunate the yellow-bellies are competent swimmers because they are sometimes forced to cross snow-laden streams to reach their feeding grounds.

Although young rockchucks are exceedingly tame, the adults are sensitive to danger, and should a circling eagle or questing badger be spotted, one sharp whistle is sufficient to send every member of the colony to shelter.

Personality

Ernest Thompson Seton, in his book *Lives of Game Animals* wrote of the yellow-bellied marmot:

High on some sunny crag that gives full fifty miles of view, the Rockchucks lie in the morning. There is nothing in their colour or habits that suggests concealment. You can see the gleaming golden mantles half a mile away. But their eyes are as sharp as yours. Many sad experiences have taught their tribe that a man on foot is a man with a far-killer . . . and instantly the sprawling watchers are alert. A shrill, short whistle each sends forth, and every Marmot on this rock and every rock for half a mile, is keen agog, or rushes coverward to some safe hiding place.

Habitat

The yellow-bellied marmot prefers open, rock-strewn terrain adjacent to lush meadows. Talus slopes at the base of mountains, jumbles of rock near forest edges, even abandoned mining shacks in a fertile valley are typical sites for a colony. In southern Alberta, they are also found in coulees beside some of the rivers.

Not all burrows in a marmot colony are used constantly. Some are "home" burrows, which may be occupied by a family, or successive families, throughout the year, while others are "auxiliary" burrows used by transients, or regular members of the colony in an emergency. Home burrows have a minimum of two entrances, while auxiliary burrows frequently lack a second entrance.

Because the yellow-belly spends up to 80 per cent of his life in his den, it is sited and excavated with special care. Normally, since a gradient for good drainage is essential, the den is dug into the side of a slope, or situated among rocks on a hillside, with the nesting chamber usually located on higher ground than the main entrance. Whenever possible, he restricts the size of the entrance by burrowing under a rock crevice, or by digging between boulders. This is a safety precaution to prevent predators like the grizzly bear and the badger from digging him out of his sanctuary. Boulders at the entrance also serve as sun-decks and observation platforms.

A Main entrance
B Secondary entrance (often hidden)
C Main passage
D Nest

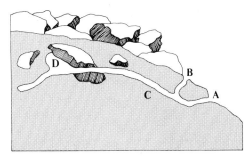

Feeding Habits

The yellow-bellied marmot starts his day in a lesurely fashion. He emerges from his den around eight o'clock, when the sun is well up, and spends the next half-hour observing the countryside and grooming himself. Then he sets off down one of the paths radiating from his burrow to a feeding area, which may be a patch of sedge, wild clover, dandelion or, if the colony is located near civilization, someone's vegetable garden. During the next two hours he will feed steadily, pausing from time to time to look up and check for danger. The balance of the morning and the early afternoon will be spent back at his den. If the weather is inclement he will stay inside, if it is fine he will probably sunbathe on an adjacent rock. Late in the day he will make a second, shorter, feeding expedition and will return to his burrow before sunset.

Life Cycle

Yellow-bellied marmots are sexually mature at two years of age, but most don't mate until their third year. Mating commences as soon as they emerge from hibernation in late March or April, depending upon the altitude. The period of gestation is approximately 30 days, and the litter numbers between 3 and 8 pups, with the average being 5.

The young, who are born blind and hairless, spend the first four weeks of their lives in the burrow. In the fifth week their mother takes them out of the den for short periods, weaning them a few days later. When they are very small, the mother moves them by carrying one pup at a time, holding each one in her mouth by the nape of its neck.

An interesting observation was made by the naturalist James Nee who noticed that when he gripped the nape of a rockchuck's neck, or even placed his hand on the nape, the animal became docile. This may be a conditioned reflex going back to the time when a marmot is carried by its mother, who certainly wouldn't want her pup to squirm!

Young marmots feed heavily and grow rapidly during the short summer. Hibernation is later for pups than for adults; the young either share a burrow with their mother, or occupy a modest den nearby.

The second year is decisive in the life of a yellow-bellied marmot; it will either become an accepted member of the colony or be forced to leave. Many females stay, but most males become transients, and many perish before they find a more hospitable colony.

Yellow-bellied marmots normally go into hibernation at the beginning of August; the precise time is governed by the altitude, the state of the weather, and the status of the animal. Adult males are the first to hibernate, while adult females and their pups may wait until the end of August or the beginning of September.

Since the hibernating den (hibernaculum) must be sited where it will be well covered with snow, it may not be the same burrow the family occupied during the summer. A thick layer of snow is important because it provides excellent insulation, and helps to keep the temperature of the sleeping chamber above freezing throughout the winter. Heavy snow does not deter the marmot's emergence in the spring; cases have been recorded of rockchucks tunneling through 3 m of wind-packed snow.

Upon entering his hibernaculum, a yellow-belly plugs the entrance to his sleeping chamber with dried grass and earth; this helps to foil predators, and provides additional insulation. Then he curls up and remains in a torpor, except for periodic arousals, until seven months of winter have slipped away.

Few people have seen a yellow-bellied marmot in hibernation. Therefore, the account of an American naturalist who came upon one sleeping in the Silver Mountain Tunnel in Colorado, may be of interest (Seton 1929:348):

[*He*] *had packed in grass for a nest, and taken up his winter quarters. He was rolled up like a ball, with his fore paws over his eyes. We pulled his paws away, and his eyes were closed. All our efforts to awake him were futile; he would yawn like a boy that had been disturbed when sleeping soundly, return his paws to his eyes, and curl himself up in his original position.*

Natural Enemies

Possibly the most devastating enemy is Nature; a winter with little snow, or a premature thaw, may cause some yellow-bellied marmots to freeze to death in their hibernating dens.

The chief threat from the air is the majestic Golden Eagle. Allan Brooks, quoted in Ernest Thompson Seton's *Lives of Game Animals*, estimated that 90 per cent of the Golden Eagle's summer diet is furnished by marmots.

On the ground they are vulnerable to "diggers" like the badger and the grizzly bear, as well as wolves and cougars. Most of the predator toll is sustained by immature animals and transients in search of another colony.

Relations with Humans

Man has had relatively little influence on this species because its habitat is not suitable for cultivation, and most colonies are remote from civilization.

The yellow-bellied marmot has been identified as an involuntary link in the transmittal of Rocky Mountain spotted fever. The germs of this dangerous disease, which can be contracted by both man and domestic animals, are carried by *Dermacentor andersoni* ticks that frequently attach themselves to rock-chucks. For this reason, care must be taken if you handle this marmot, and it should be noted that some ground squirrels and chipmunks also harbour this tick.

Because the fur of the yellow-bellied marmot is not used commercially, this species is considered to have no economic value. However, it is impossible to ignore the aesthetic value of watching these hardy animals in their natural environment.

Where to Observe

National Parks in the mountains of southern Alberta and British Columbia have colonies of yellow-bellied marmots that may be seen on guided tours with the park naturalist. In Manning Provincial Park, British Columbia, it is possible to view the marmots from your car, as a number of animals have made dens in the rocky embankment of the highway.

Hoary Marmot
Marmotte des Rocheuses
Marmota caligata

Common Names

Like the other marmots in Canada, the hoary marmot communicates by whistling, but he is the champion whistler of them all. For this reason, he has been called the mountain whistler, white whistler, grey whistler, whistler of the rocks, and *le siffleur* "whistler" in French.

His scientific name ignores his vocal prowess, and refers instead to the contrast between his light coat and dark feet, *Marmota caligata* being Latin for "booted marmot".

Description

The hoary marmot, although he is built like a woodchuck, is actually twice the woodchuck's size, making him the largest of the Sciuridae in Canada. An adult male can weigh up to 13 kg, and attain an overall length of 80 cm. However, the average weight for a male is closer to 6 kg, and the female is smaller.

Although he has a lot of white in his coat, and a frosty "stole" covering his back and shoulders, he is difficult to spot at a distance because, like the camouflage of a battleship, his colour scheme breaks his outline, and he blends with the rocks.

His distinctive, multi-coloured head has a black "cap", dark streaks on the sides, and a white patch on the muzzle. His hindquarters, which are a warm cinnamon colour, match the orange lichen on boulders, while his short, bushy tail is brown, and his paws are black. Because these marmots vary considerably in their pelage, the foregoing is a general, but reasonably typical, description. Melanistic specimens have been recorded, and seem to occur most frequently in the northern part of his range.

Hoary Marmot

Canadian Range

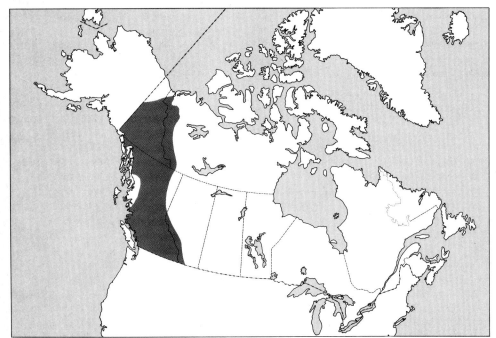

Range

In Canada, the hoary marmot flourishes in the Rocky Mountains, extending through Alberta, British Columbia, the Northwest Territories, and the Yukon. His widely spaced colonies are usually found in alpine tundra, at elevations ranging from 1800 to 4000 m. However, because tree-line descends as it goes north, Alaska has hoary marmot colonies at less than 100 m above sea level. Despite this phenomenon, the average altitude in the Canadian range is around 2000 m.

Behaviour

Hoary marmots live in colonies consisting of a few polygamous males, one of whom is dominant, and many females. Like their cousins the yellow-bellied marmots, they have a pecking order, but hoary marmots differ from the yellow-bellies in that they seem more tolerant of each other, and less sensitive to the violation of territories within the colony.

There is a great deal of social contact within the colony; tail flagging, nuzzling, and playful combat are prevalent, but true agonistic behaviour is relatively rare. Indeed, not only the young, but adults of both sexes appear to enjoy stand-up boxing and wrestling matches. Often these contests take place on a hillside and both animals end up rolling hurly-burly down the slope—at the bottom they disengage, and climb back up for another round.

These marmots are famous for their piercing alarm whistle, which is well described by A.W.F. Banfield in his book *The Mammals of Canada*:
. . . a long shrill whistle, almost exactly the same pitch and duration as the familiar police whistle. This always has a startling effect upon the visitor, who immediately assumes he is being called by someone in an apparently lonely land.

Since the whistle has a tremendous carrying quality and reverberates around the empty cirque, it is difficult to locate the whistler.

The short alarm call is only one of several in a hoary marmot's repertoire; the others vary in pitch, volume, and frequency. Like a well-trained opera singer, he produces these sounds from his chest and throat with such control that he can continue for long periods. Dr. David Gray of the National Museum of Natural Sciences recorded 959 whistles from a single marmot in the space of 32 minutes!

He is a diurnal mammal, spending much of his day outside, feeding, socializing, or relaxing near his burrow. Although he is hardy, and stays outside through light rain or even hail storms, he may be driven to seek shelter in his den by intense heat or a sudden onslaught of flies or mosquitoes.

This wary rock dweller is an excellent climber, and can move with surprising speed and agility when pressed.

Personality

During the summer of 1966, Dr. David Gray made a comprehensive study of a colony of hoary marmots in Manning Provincial Park, British Columbia. Two of his favourite subjects were a male and a female that he named Darkchest and Whiteface:
Whiteface lacked the typical dark markings on her head, and her beautiful white mantle extended over much of her body. Darkchest, on the other hand, had little white on his shoulders and was very dark underneath. Often, while resting on a burrow mound, Whiteface and Darkchest would lie together, one on top, with paws draped over the other.

In this position they sometimes groomed each other, biting gently at the fur on the back or head of the other. Few marmots in the colony had such a close relationship. In late June and early July, in encounters with Darkchest, (Whiteface's partner in most social interactions), their initial greeting was usually followed by a wrestling match. This playful wrestling usually lasted several minutes, and was the main feature of fully one-third of the social encounters between Whiteface and other marmots. Well over half of these involved Darkchest as wrestling partner. However, by late July, something had changed, and poor old Darkchest was left following the aloof Whiteface, ineffectively batting and biting at her in a vain attempt to initiate the playful wrestling that occupied so many of their hours in early summer.

Habitat

The hoary marmot's favourite habitat is near or even above tree-line, in a talus or a boulder-filled alpine meadow, at altitudes of around 2000 m. Little is known about the interior of his burrow, whose entrance is usually sited among large rocks. By digging his burrow deep under a sheltering boulder, he protects himself from attack by large predators such as the grizzly bear, as well as cannily providing himself with a combination observation post and sun-deck.

In a typical colony there will be many more burrows than there are marmots. This suggests that some are "home" burrows, where the young are raised, others are "sleeping" burrows, which may be occupied from time to time; and most are "auxiliary" burrows, which are only used as a refuge in an emergency.

The hoary marmot is an efficient digger who not only excavates with all four feet, but also uses his mouth to carry small stones out of the tunnel.

Feeding Habits

Hoary marmots are herbivores who have two main feeding periods each day; the first and longest takes place shortly after they emerge from their burrows, the second a few hours before sundown. They are mobile foragers who ramble along with frequent pauses to look about, or to sit up and chew. Normally they crop the vegetation with their teeth and then hold it in their paws to eat. Sometimes they stuff their mouths with grasses, which they carry back to their dens for use as a lining. Staples of their diet are: grasses, roots, wild flowers, berries, and a broad spectrum of alpine greens.

This marmot may range up to 200 m from his den, and is particularly susceptible to the pull of a lush but distant feeding patch. In fact, his appetite is his Achilles heel, because it causes him to stray from the safety of the colony; the further he travels, the more vulnerable he is to predators, especially the Golden Eagle.

Life Cycle

Snow is still deep in the high country when these marmots emerge from hibernation during April or May. This doesn't deter them, nor does it cool their ardour, for they mate soon after emergence. The period of gestation is estimated at between 28 and 30 days, and the litter is usually 4 or 5 pups. The young remain inside the home burrow with their mother until they are approximately one month old.

Life in the colony is sociable, and all ages seem to get along with a minimum of friction. Feeding is an important part of their daily routine, as it is essential for them to build a thick layer of fat if they are to survive the winter. Another priority is the security of the community; at any one time at least one marmot will be alert to potential danger and his warning whistle is heeded by everyone.

Although hoary marmots feed voraciously, and put on a great deal of weight during the summer, their feeding activity tapers off in the weeks just prior to hibernation. One explanation for this contradictory behaviour is that the reduction in their daily activity and food intake serves to precondition them for hibernation, slowing their metabolism, and causing anorexia (loss of appetite).

They hibernate for approximately seven months, with the old males and barren females entering their dens in September. Fertile adult females and their offspring remain active until late September or the beginning of October. This staggered schedule is undoubtedly Nature's way of giving the pups extra time to grow and fatten before their first, and most hazardous, year of hibernation.

The young are only half grown by their first autumn, and frequently hibernate in the same den as their mother. By the end of the second summer, when they are fully grown, they usually establish their own burrows.

Natural Enemies

The chief predators of the hoary marmot are the grizzly bear and the Golden Eagle. During the summer, the Golden Eagle can drop like a thunderbolt on those who stray too far from their den, as well as those enjoying the apparent safety of a sunning pinnacle. The grizzly is a threat because he is the only animal with sufficient strength to dig a marmot out of his den.

Relations with Humans

The hoary marmot has suffered relatively little human interference because his habitat is remote, and he is extremely alert; a trait that was noted by one of Canada's leading naturalists, J. Dewey Soper, in his book *The Mammals of Alberta:*

Like all of the marmots, those of the northern Rockies are amazingly wary creatures. At a very respectable distance the big, vigilant sentinels perch on prominent boulders for the detection of any intruders in their territory. At the first resounding whistle of alarm the whole neighbouring clan dashes off wildly to nearby retreats. Here at the entrances the animals resume the lynx-eyed watchfulness; at the first sign of danger a head-long plunge is made into their holes. This super cautiousness renders the animals difficult to collect with a gun . . .

In the past, the hoary marmot's flesh was relished by Indians and mountain men, who also used his dense pelt to make garments and sleeping robes. Now, with the availability of packaged foods and insulated clothing, he is rarely hunted.

Other marmots are not so fortunate. Alpine marmots in parts of Europe are still killed for their fat, which is sold as a sovereign remedy against rheumatism and respiratory ailments. Uneducated people purchase this oil in the erroneous belief that marmot fat must contain special properties because marmots spend long months in their damp, cold dens without ill effect. The trade peaked for this product in 1944 when an estimated 16,000 marmots were killed in Switzerland alone. Since then, public education programmes sponsored by conservation groups have reduced the demand for marmot oil.

Where to Observe

If you visit one of the national parks in the mountains of Alberta or British Columbia, the park naturalist can arrange for you to accompany a guided tour, or direct you to a hiking trail that passes by a marmot colony.

Vancouver Island Marmot
Marmotte de l'île Vancouver
Marmota vancouverensis

Common Names

Most people on the West Coast simply refer to him as the marmot, although some loggers in the high country affectionately call him the little brown pig.

His scientific name, *Marmota vancouverensis*, is a combination of Latin and fabricated Latin; *Marmota* means marmot (literally, mountain mouse), while *vancouverensis* is the name of the island, with *ensis* tacked on. Latinizing the location, or the name of the discoverer, is a favourite method taxonomists use when classifying a particular species; the ending depends upon the case and gender.

Description

The Vancouver Island marmot is similar in many ways to his cousin the hoary marmot, but he is slightly smaller, his colouring is different, and his snout has a distinctive bone structure.

In July, when the Vancouver Island marmot has completed his annual moult, his coat is a lustrous black, relieved by a white ring around his muzzle, a white patch on his forehead, and white streaks along his chest and belly. As the summer progresses, his fur gradually fades to a rich chocolate-brown; by the following spring it is a dull-cinnamon colour. Regardless of the stage of the moult, he is difficult to spot at a distance because the shades of his coat blend naturally with the lichen-covered rocks.

These marmots usually double, and sometimes triple, their weight from May until September; by July, adult males average 4.5 kg, while mature females average around 3.75 kg. Although females consistently weigh less than males, both sexes attain an overall length of approximately 67 cm.

Vancouver Island Marmot

Canadian Range

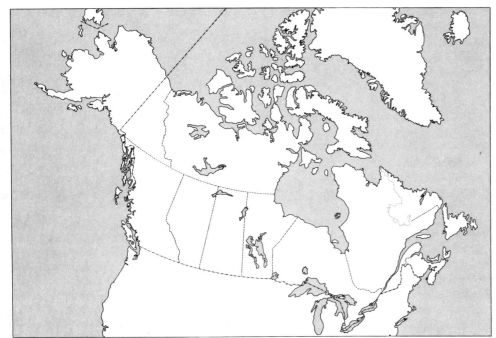

Range
The only place in the world the Vancouver Island marmot is found is on Vancouver Island. This species lives in the subalpine mountainous regions on the western side of the island, and favours slopes with a southern exposure. There are 26 known colonies, some of which have been in existence for many years. A typical colony will occupy approximately 2.5 ha, and have 8 members. The total population, allowing for undiscovered colonies, is estimated to be less than 1,000 animals.

Behaviour

This marmot lives in small colonies that, in the spring, often consist of one adult male, an adult female, and a number of two year olds and yearlings of both sexes. If it is a breeding year for the adult female, the colony will be increased by 3 or 4 infants in June.

Vancouver Island marmots live in relative harmony, even delaying dispersal of the young until their third summer. Agonistic behaviour is not a serious factor, but the marmots are territorial, and mature members take care to mark their boundaries frequently by leaving scent from their cheek glands on prominent rocks. They also have a pecking order, or scale of dominance, which is invariably headed by an adult male, followed by the adult females, then the two-year-old males, two-year-old females, yearling males, and at the bottom, yearling females. This may appear to be a chauvinistic hierarchy, where the males always take precedence, but by far the most aggressive members are the adult females.

By nature these marmots are very sociable, and this is particularly noticeable during the first six weeks after they emerge from hibernation; one explanation is that they may be getting to know each other again after an eight-month absence. Most social encounters are characterized by tail waving similar to a housecat's, nose-to-nose greetings, or playfights. Playfights are really shoving matches in which both contestants stand on their hind legs and push their opponent in the chest with their forepaws. Many greetings are brief; both parties continue on their separate ways almost immediately.

Although his vocal repertoire includes hissing, growling, and chattering, the Vancouver Island marmot is best known for his whistle, which sounds like someone blowing into the top of an empty cartridge. The main purpose of his whistle is to alert the colony to danger; the louder the note, the greater the peril. Even when you are watching a colony, it is difficult locate the source of a whistle; the rocks are part of the reason because they create an echo, but the main cause is the narrow bandwidth of the sound. The narrow frequency of the whistle helps to protect the marmot from predators, especially eagles, hawks, and owls, whose extremely sensitive hearing permits them to pinpoint broad bandwidth sounds with uncanny precision.

Studies by Douglas Heard, Canada's leading authority on the Vancouver Island marmot, suggest that these marmots use a long whistle, lasting about one second, as a warning against predators on the ground, and a shorter one, more of a pip, when the danger is in the sky. The animal who spies an intruder normally heads straight for his den; once there, he stops and whistles to alert the colony. Those in the open make for their dens, but pause to identify the threat before disappearing; those who are in their burrows peek out for the same reason. This behaviour is prudent because identification of the predator will tell them what to expect when they re-emerge; for instance, a cougar may still be waiting in ambush, while an eagle will probably drift off to greener pastures.

Personality

During two summers spent observing marmot colonies in the Green Mountain area of British Columbia, Douglas Heard got to know the behaviour of many of his subjects. Recently, he wrote me about one of his favourites:

"Light-tail", an adult male, attracted my attention early in the season, because he was continually patrolling his territory. When other marmots were having a sunbath, or simply admiring the view from a prominent rock, he would be dutifully making his rounds. Light-tail would move purposefully from tree stump, to rock, to burrow entrance, stopping only to scent mark or to greet a neighbour.

Sometimes he would compose himself comfortably on a rock and I would think that at last he was going to stop fretting, and relax. But a moment or two later he would be up and away to check his boundaries.

Eventually it happened. In midsummer Light-tail was confronted by another adult male who obviously planned to take up residence on his property. I thought there would be a vicious scuffle, but Light-tail chose a peaceful solution. He allowed the interloper to stake a small piece of ground, and then ignored that part of the meadow—and its new occupant—for the rest of the summer.

Habitat

The marmots of Vancouver Island live in small colonies on the subalpine slopes and open meadows at altitudes from 1100 to 1500 m. Since the high country receives up to 300 cm of snow in an average winter, the marmots favour steep (30° to 70°) slopes with a southern exposure; the steep inclines shed the snow, and the sun stimulates the early growth of vegetation. Frequently, this type of terrain is subject to avalanches, which not only clear the snow with a rush, but sweep away large trees so that low bushes and plants get a chance to grow. Thus, avalanches benefit the habitat, but present no hazard to the marmots, for they occur while the marmots are safely hibernating in their burrows.

Frequently, Vancouver Island marmots construct burrows in crevices among the jumbled rocks of a talus, or like the woodchuck, they dig a den in an open meadow where there are no rocks. However, the most typical site is beneath a huge boulder, whose shadow will hide several bolt holes.

Little is known about the interior of the burrow except that late in the day marmots often collect dead grass and sedges to take back to their den; these are probably used to line the sleeping chamber. It is not unusual for several animals, particularly a male and a female, to occupy the same burrow.

Feeding Habits

When these marmots emerge in May they face a scarcity of food because of the deep snow, and because the growing season has barely started. During May they spend up to 40 per cent of their day foraging on the windswept slopes and cliffs; the staples of their diet at this time are winter-preserved *Kinnikinnick* berries, as well as the roots and bark of huckleberry and cedar. By June, greenery is thriving on the meadows and they extend their menu by including the leaves and flowers of many other plants. In August, food is everywhere, "the living is easy", and they can concentrate on the most nutritious items, flowers and berries, feeding for less than 20 per cent of their day.

During the cool months of May and September, they may feed at any hour. During the warm months of June, July, and August, or whenever the temperature exceeds 20°C, they stop feeding and retire to their burrows in the late morning and early afternoon. Unlike some of their cousins, they rarely use their paws when eating; all their grazing is done with their teeth. Some of their other favourite foods are: the leaves and flowers of the cow-parsnip; flowers of the spreading phlox, Indian paintbrush, and tiger lily; and blueberry and huckleberry fruit.

Life Cycle

These hardy creatures sometimes have to tunnel out of deep snow when they emerge from their dens in May. Mating takes place at the first opportunity, but there is reason to believe that adult females only reproduce every second year, the average litter being 3 pups. In addition, since this species is slow to mature, most don't breed until their fourth summer. Thus the birth rate in a colony is always low.

Marmots of the season are usually first seen outside their mother's burrow at the beginning of July; they look like miniature adults with jet-black coats, which they retain all summer. Yearlings and older animals complete their moult in July, but their ebony coats fade to dark brown by September.

Because of the severe weight loss induced by hibernation, their prime objective during the short alpine summer is to gain as much weight as possible, so they can survive the coming winter. In the early spring, when feeding areas are limited by snow, all members of the colony share the same feeding area.

However, from the end of June, when the snow melts, territories are staked and boundaries are strictly enforced. Although adult females engage in agonistic behaviour by chasing away intruders, and strictly policing their territories, it is unusual for a colony's adult males to have a confrontation. In fact, the males make a point of avoiding a showdown even though the dispersal of males doesn't usually take place until they are three years old. The timetable for dispersal is probably connected with the slowness of this species to mature; only full-grown animals have a reasonable chance of surviving the quest for a suitable place to settle.

There is a marked decline in the feeding and daily activities of these marmots during the weeks prior to hibernation. By the end of September, they will have doubled their weight, and most will have completed their moult. Those that haven't completed their moult enter hibernation in the transitional stage, and don't resume their change of fur until the next July.

By the end of September, the infants will weigh approximately 1 kg, and will hibernate the first winter with their mother.

It is reasonable to assume that their hibernation timetable is similar to that of other marmots, with the mature males and barren females being the first to enter their dens, and the young of the year, with their mothers, the last. The average length of hibernation is seven to eight months; roughly from the first of October to the first of May.

Natural Enemies

The Golden Eagle is capable of snatching a full-grown marmot, while the Red-tailed Hawk is a threat to the young. On land, these marmots' main enemies are the cougar and the black bear; the grizzly bear is not present on Vancouver Island.

Relations with Humans

Because of its remote habitat, this species has suffered relatively little from the inroads of civilization; colonies on lumber-company land are not usually disturbed because the avalanche-prone terrain the marmots favour grows insufficient trees to merit cutting.

Undoubtedly some marmots have been killed by rifle shooters, but only 30 have been collected for scientific purposes in the last 70 years, and the public is now aware of the need to protect them.

The Vancouver Island marmot is a unique Canadian species; as such it is of inestimable value.

Where to Observe

This wary marmot lives in the subalpine highlands; to observe him properly you will have to do some hiking, and use binoculars. Pause frequently to listen; almost invariably his alarm whistle is the first clue to his presence. For the location of a colony in the Green Mountain area of British Columbia, contact the British Columbia Fish and Wildlife branch at Nanaimo.

Black-tailed Prairie Dog
Chien de prairie
Cynomys ludovicianus

Common Names

His most common nickname is the prairie dog. Because of his distinctive call, he has also been known as the prairie barker, barking ground squirrel, and barking marmot.

This little rodent's scientific name, *Cynomys ludovicianus*, is a combination of Greek and Latin words. *Cynomys* is Greek meaning "dog-mouse", while *ludovicianus* is Latin for Louisiana. The Latin indicated his range, the gigantic territory west of the Mississippi known as the Louisiana Purchase, when this species was identified in 1804 by Meriwether Lewis, of the Lewis and Clark Expedition.

Description

The black-tailed prairie dog resembles a heavyset ground squirrel, having very short ears and a skimpy tail. His dense coat blends with the sunbaked terrain because it is a pinkish-tan colour except for the pale-buff underparts and black-tipped tail.

Size varies with age, sex, and the time of year. As a rule, males are heavier than females, although both sexes attain an overall length of approximately 38 cm. The average weight for an adult male is 1.35 kg, while an adult female weighs closer to 1.25 kg.

This species moults twice each year, in the spring and the autumn. Because of the short summer in the northern part of the range, moulting is an ongoing process, with one phase gradually blending into the other. In the spring moult, fur replenishment begins at the chest and works toward the tail; the autumn moult moves in the opposite direction, from the hindquarters to the head.

The colour of the black-tailed prairie dog's pelage is remarkably uniform, and melanistic or albino animals are rare.

Black-tailed Prairie Dog

Canadian Range

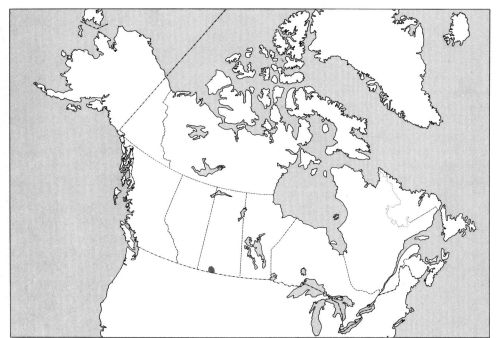

Range

The range of the black-tailed prairie dog in Canada is restricted to a tiny area near the town of Val Marie, in southern Saskatchewan. Most of the colonies are situated in the valley of the Frenchman River, or its tributaries, within a 50 km radius of Val Marie. Because this represents the northern tip of the continental population, the average density is only 20 animals to the hectare; in the centre of its range there can be as many as 85 to the hectare.

Although the area had been settled for many years, it wasn't until 1927 that this species was identified by a Canadian naturalist, J. Dewey Soper. The animals were given no protection until 1965, when the Saskatchewan Natural History Society established a sanctuary.

Since their discovery, the prairie dogs have extended their range so that the several thousand Canadian members of the species now occupy more than a dozen colonies.

Behaviour

Prairie dogs are gregarious animals who live in densely populated colonies or "towns" that can sprawl over many hectares. These towns are subdivided into much smaller units known as "coteries", which consist of 2 to 30 members, and usually occupy less than 0.50 ha.

Each coterie is a closed society whose members live in harmony, bound by ties of affection and loyalty for each other, and a mutual dislike for everyone else. There is no pecking order within the coterie, except for the recognition of one dominant male. This dominant male is the first to emerge from his burrow in the morning and the last to retire at night; in the interim he checks on all members of the clan, and leads the attack on anyone who intrudes on their territory. Although boundary skirmishes are an everyday occurrence in a prairie-dog town, these "fights" are rarely mortal as they consist in the main of bravado, tail waving, teeth chattering, and possibly a nip at the intruder's rear end. Indeed, the most striking aspect of behaviour within the coterie is not the aggression but the tolerance and cooperation the prairie dogs exhibit toward each other. There is a great deal of "kissing" (nose touching) and grooming, and all members share the responsibility of raising the young and maintaining the burrows. Except for dens occupied by females with litters, any burrow in the territory may be used by any member of the coterie. Because most of the dens are connected by subterranean passages, this is rather like the tenants of an apartment building giving a key to their suite to all the other occupants.

Black-tailed prairie dogs are noted for their barking cries. These range from a few sharp yips, given on the run as they head for cover, to an extended series that can last up to an hour. The bark of alarm is heeded by everyone in the immediate area, and is a vital defence against predators. The "territorial" call is often ignored, but it is such a favourite call that a prairie dog may utter it at any time of day, and he frequently uses it as an "all-clear" signal after danger has passed. To make the territorial call, he stands on his hind legs, thrusts his forepaws out, raises his nose to the sky, and emits a loud, two-note bark. His whole body is employed in the delivery, and sometimes he calls with such exuberance that he falls over backwards, making one wonder if it isn't some form of cheer, like "hooray for our side!".

Prairie dogs are diurnal; major activities on a typical day would be feeding, socializing, and working on the burrow. They dislike stormy weather and usually remain in their burrows when it rains or is heavily overcast, reappearing only when the sun shines again. Like many other animals, they are nervous and alert when the wind blows; this may be due to the constant rustling sounds that can mask the approach of a predator.

Personality

In an article for *Nature Canada*, titled "The Prairie Dogs of Val Marie", Mrs. Jeannie Wagner of the Saskatchewan Natural History Society wrote: *Within each district the animals feed and play in a spirit of co-operative harmony and it is not uncommon to see a pair of prairie dogs exchange greetings by placing their forepaws around each other in a joyful embrace accompanied by a kiss. Affection is showered on the pups, five or six of which are born in each spring litter, by all the adults of the clan.*

Habitat

The black-tailed prairie dog is a creature of the open flats and short-grass plains, the type of country often seen in Western movies. This dry, treeless terrain is sparsely covered with low shrubs like prickly pear cactus, and sagebrush.

His habitat in Canada is the semi-arid bottomland of the Frenchman River, at altitudes between 800 and 1000 m.

Black-tailed prairie dogs live in holes dug in open, relatively flat ground. Most burrows are marked by a mound of earth with a crater-like depression leading to the entrance, or bolt hole. In Saskatchewan, average dimensions for a den mound are 0.3 m high, and 1 m across the base. Usually the bolt hole drops vertically for approximately 3 m and then branches off into one or more passages; along the passages are several rooms, including a spoil room and a sleeping chamber. The latter, which is lined with grass, measures approximately 55 cm from wall to wall, and 38 cm from floor to ceiling. Many of the burrows in a coterie are connected by subterranean passages; thus a black-tail can disappear down one bolt hole, and reappear out of another.

A feature unique to burrows of black-tailed prairie dogs is a niche in the side of the burrow, slightly below ground level. This small shelf serves as a turning point, a protected listening post in time of danger, and a hiding place when predators threaten to pursue a prairie dog down his burrow.

The mound of earth surrounding the entrance to the burrow is important because it acts as a breakwater against flash floods, and as an elevated observation platform. For these reasons, the slope and rim are kept in good repair by the animals who push the soil into place with their noses and tamp it down with their paws and foreheads; often several will work on the same burrow.

Members of a coterie may use any burrow they wish, except those occupied by females with young. Other species that use the burrows include ground squirrels, cottontail rabbits, Burrowing Owls, and snakes—the last two species being most unwelcome guests. In the past, bison would occasionally wander into a prairie-dog town and use the den craters to take a dust bath; a large herd could obliterate quite a few burrows in this way. However, this is an historical note rather than a current problem, because the herds of native bison long ago vanished from south Saskatchewan.

A Mound
B Funnel-shaped entrance
C Niche large enough for one prairie dog
D Main vertical passage
E Horizontal passage
F Nest
G Unused nests filled with grass and refuse
H Unused portion of horizontal passage filled with earth

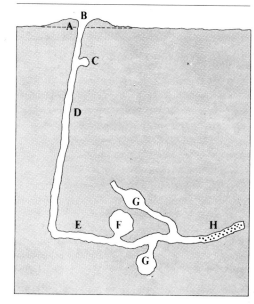

Feeding Habits

Prairie dogs are voracious eaters who spend up to 60 per cent of each summer day filling their stomachs. During the winter, they eat sparingly because of the scarcity of herbage and the restrictions imposed by the weather. Normally they crop most of the vegetation near their dens, which is not only convenient, but also ensures an unobstructed view of the surrounding countryside.

Their diet consists of a variety of grasses, sedges, and forbs (broad-leafed herbs), which they select by scent, harvest with their incisors, and eat with their paws. In addition to providing nourishment, these plants are their chief source of water; one of the best is the stalk of the thistle, which they hold near its root to avoid being pricked. Black-tailed prairie dogs are primarily herbivores, but they will eat grasshoppers and other insects when vegetation is scarce.

In normal circumstances feeding takes place throughout the day; however, extremely high temperatures or thunderstorms can drive them into their burrows. Immediately after a shower they feed hungrily; possibly the rain-freshened plants whet their appetite.

Life Cycle

In Saskatchewan, mating takes place early in April, the period of gestation is 30 to 35 days, and the young are born around the third week in May. The average litter is 5 pups, which are born blind and hairless, weighing approximately 55 g each. For the first six weeks they stay below ground with their mother. They are weaned shortly after they emerge from the burrow, in their seventh week. In their early days young prairie dogs receive a great deal of care from everyone in the coterie; they spend their days playing or eating, and by the time they are three months old they weigh around 350 g. While the first summer is probably the safest period in their lives, the first winter is the most dangerous, and many don't live to see the following spring.

The average life-expectancy for a black-tailed prairie dog in the wild is three years, although captive animals have survived for seven. Because of this short life-span, the population of a town or coterie is subject to severe fluctuations, and the deciding factor is the number of sexually mature females in any given year. In addition to mortality and the birth rate, dispersal affects the size of towns and coteries. Unlike agonistic species, which force fellow members out of the territory, prairie dogs seem to have a voluntary system of dispersal. The bulk of emigrants are restless young males who want to establish their own coterie, and adult females who may simply wish to relocate. The females usually join a nearby coterie or town; the males range further afield, and theirs is a far more hazardous trek.

Although dispersal depletes the already small number of prairie dogs, it also expands their range, prevents overgrazing, and avoids overcrowding with the attendant possibility of disease.

Unlike marmots, black-tailed prairie dogs are not true hibernators, but their activity is greatly reduced, and they often stay in their dens for days at a time. Their feeding is restricted to sunny days when the snow is not too deep, although cold doesn't seem to bother them, possibly because of their dense coat. However, the scarcity of food makes it imperative that they build a heavy layer of fat in the summer if they are to survive the harsh winter months.

Natural Enemies

The prairie dog has a host of enemies. He is attacked from the sky by eagles, hawks, and owls; on land by bobcats, foxes, and coyotes; below the ground by badgers, ferrets, and snakes. His only effective defence is a well-developed alarm system, but each predator takes its toll. One persistent myth is that he lives in harmony with rattlesnakes and the Burrowing Owl. Ernest Thompson Seton denounced this fable more than half a century ago, and another naturalist (Hollister 1916:7), summed up the relationship of the trio with these words:

Many absurd stories of the joint occupation of dens by prairie dogs, rattlesnakes, and burrowing owls have been written, but careful observers have found that whatever the relation between these denizens of the plain may be—and the creatures are often found together in the villages—it is anything but advantageous to the prairie dog, and large numbers of its young are destroyed by the unwelcome visitors.

Relations with Humans

As Man moved west, he improved the habitat for the prairie dog, and killed most of the predators. In consequence, these rodents flourished; Seton estimated their number at the turn of the century to be five billion. Then, when they came in direct conflict with the aspirations of farmers and ranchers, the result was a widespread and systematic campaign to eradicate the species. Initial results were unsatisfactory, but strychnine-loaded grain proved a great success, and the chemical 1080, introduced after World War II, proved even more lethal. One side-effect of the poisoning campaign has been the near-extinction of the black-footed ferret, which fed on prairie dogs and was also poisoned.

Except for the efforts of some conservation groups and a few enlightened individuals, the influence of Man on the black-tailed prairie dog has been consistently bad. In certain localities, the black-tailed prairie dog has been a pest to the agricultural community by eating crops, and to the cattle industry by consuming some of the graze. In addition, their holes are a hazard to horses and cattle.

On the plus side, they are a functional part of the environment as they provide food for predators, and shelter for other species.

Currently, they are considered to have no economic value, although they were eaten by some Plains Indians in the past.

Where to Observe

The only place in Canada where black-tailed prairie dogs live in the wild is the Val Marie district of southern Saskatchewan. The best way to see them is to visit the Prairie Dog Sanctuary; for specific directions contact the Saskatchewan Natural History Society in Regina, or the Val Marie Chamber of Commerce.

They may also be observed in captivity, as a fair number of Canadian zoos have this species in their collections.

Richardson's Ground Squirrel
Spermophile de Richardson
Spermophilus richardsonii

Common Names

Most people refer to the Richardson's ground squirrel as a gopher. However, this is incorrect because gophers are members of a different family, the Geomyidae.

He has two other descriptive nicknames: picket pin and flickertail. He is called a picket pin because, when standing on the prairie, he looks like one of the pegs used by plainsmen to tether their horses. Flickertail is also appropriate; he twitches his tail so frequently that one oldtimer made the observation that his voice and his tail are connected—whenever he raises one, he raises the other.

His scientific name, *Spermophilus richardsonii*, is a combination of Greek and fabricated Latin. *Spermophilus* is Greek for "lover of seeds", while *richardsonii* is the Latinized surname of Sir John Richardson who discovered the species in 1820 near Carlton House, Saskatchewan, while acting as surgeon-naturalist for Sir John Franklin's expedition to find the Northwest Passage.

Description

He has the outline of a plump squirrel with a short, flat tail. From a distance he appears beige, but at close range his coat is yellow along the sides, brownish on the back, and pale grey or buff on the underparts. His large eyes are set high in his skull permitting him to spot airborne predators with a minimum of movement, and to scan the countryside from his hole with only the crown of his head exposed.

Male Richardson's ground squirrels are larger than females, but both sexes attain a similar overall length of approximately 32 cm. During the spring and summer, adults feed heavily, and may increase their body weight from 300 g to more than 450 g; the average weight of an adult in July would be around 350 g.

Richardson's Ground Squirrel

Canadian Range

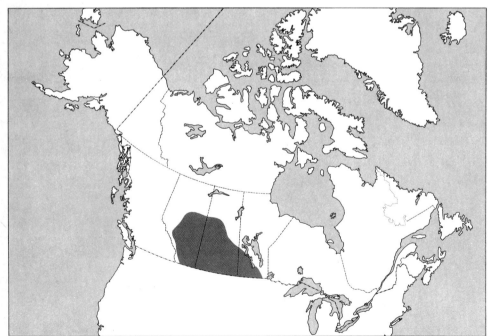

Range

Richardson's ground squirrels live on the prairies and open flatlands in the southern portions of Manitoba, Saskatchewan, and Alberta. Their numbers vary with the terrain, and the normal density for a colony ranges between 5 to 20 animals to the hectare.

Most authorities agree that their range has increased since the West was settled and the land cleared of trees. However, it should be noted that the highest populations occur in virgin grassland, rather than in cultivated areas.

Behaviour

The animals dwell in rambling colonies where each female has her own territory, and individual members seldom stray more than 50 m from their home burrow. Their social structure is based on the family unit of a female and her young, rather than the coterie, and they are indifferent or openly hostile to everyone else in the colony.

Because of their independent and frequently antisocial behaviour, it is reasonable to wonder why they choose to live in colonies. The answer may be that it increases the individual's chances for survival by providing many sentinels (warning whistles are heeded regardless of their source), as well as a multiple choice of victims for predators.

The young of this species mature as yearlings, and disperse shortly after they emerge from hibernation. Dispersal is not forced by agonistic behaviour, although mothers treat their sons coolly while remaining on warm terms with their daughters. For this reason, many yearling females settle close to home, and most young males disperse to more-distant sites.

Richardson's ground squirrels are diurnal, but intense heat or rain will drive them to the shelter of their dens; like humans they prefer to be out in clear weather with moderate temperatures.

They are most active in the spring and early summer. However, as the time for hibernation approaches they become increasingly lethargic and by the end of August, all are below ground.

Personality

Ernest Thompson Seton wrote in *Life Histories of Northern Animals* (1909:391–92):

If you walk gently toward a Ground-squirrel sitting at his front door, he gives a short, husky whistle about every ten seconds, jerks up his tail-end in time to his music, then takes the sub-soil plunge . . . His short whistle is invariably heard within, once or twice; then his nose reappears, only to drop back when he sees you. But he returns; and if you are still, he gets bolder, popping back and forth, probably; and though you be but three feet from the mouth, he will dodge out and scuttle away to the next burrow. It looks like a piece of daredevil bravado, for in many cases, there was reason to suppose he was the owner of the hole he was leaving, and was not driven forth by any inhospitable relative.

Habitat

Richardson's ground squirrel is a true prairie dweller, favouring open, treeless stretches and rolling plains where the soil is relatively dry. His native habitat is virgin prairie with unbroken sod, but he is also found in grassland, abandoned farmland, cultivated fields, and irrigated land.

Whenever possible, he will take advantage of a ridge or fold in the ground for a den site, providing it is adjacent to a good food supply.

This squirrel's home is usually dug into a rise of ground close to the main food source. Normally, the tunnel enters the soil on a diagonal, and then branches off into a maze of passages, galleries, and chambers, which may extend for more than 15 m. These passages frequently run on two levels, incorporating blind alleys, one or more storerooms, and a sleeping chamber whose average dimensions are 23 cm across and 15 cm high. Some of the these passages lead to carefully concealed bolt holes, which can be more than 10 m from the prominent earth mound of the main entrance. Because this species is not very quick on its feet, especially just prior to hibernation when it is very fat, these bolt holes can save its life in an emergency.

Feeding Habits

Richardson's ground squirrels are omnivores who prefer to eat vegetation, but they also eat grasshoppers and other insects, and are not above cannibalizing their road-killed brethren.

Their main feeding periods are the early hours of the morning, just after sunup; from around 10 a.m. until 2 p.m.; and the hour before sunset. Although most of their foraging is done with their teeth, they sometimes hold their food in their paws to eat it. Because of the severe weight loss from hibernation, they are voracious feeders in the early summer; favourite items in their diet are wild onions, sage, pigweed, and wild sunflowers.

For several weeks prior to hibernation, their food consumption declines, but they continue to fill their cheeks with seeds, which they transfer to their burrow. Their stretchy cheek pouches have an extraordinary capacity, and are capable of holding several hundred grains of wheat or oats at a time. When they eventually curl up for the winter, their larder may contain several pails of seeds.

Most feeding takes place within 100 m of the burrow; by the end of the summer, well-worn paths radiate from its entrance to the best grazing patches.

Life Cycle

Emergence varies across the prairies, usually taking place from mid-March to the beginning of April. One key factor is the weather; when the temperature stays above freezing for several days in a row, it is likely to stimulate the animals into leaving their burrows. Like the marmots, old males are the first to emerge from hibernation.

In a normal year, mating takes place during April, and the young are born approximately 24 days later. An average litter consists of 8 pups and the young, which are born blind and hairless, each weigh around 6 g. Four or five weeks after their birth, the infants emerge from their mother's den, looking like tiny replicas of their parents.

For the next month they are closely supervised by their mother, who watches over them from the vantage point of a ridge or the mound of earth at the entrance of the burrow. If she feels the natal den is no longer secure, she will not hesitate to carry them by the scruff of the neck to a safer hole. It is a common sight to see the mother on her hind legs, like a picket pin, surrounded by six or eight little ones sunning and playing at her feet. During this period the young learn the boundaries of the family territory the hard way—by being chased by neighbours when they stray from their home territory. At ten weeks, they begin to participate aggressively in territorial disputes, but it is unusual for adults to take much notice of them.

May is the time of dispersal for yearlings, but June is the most active month socially in a Richardson's colony, as well as the peak feeding period. Most yearling females settle near their home burrow, but the males set off on much longer journeys, and many die along the way. The heavy loss of yearling males, which may seem a cruel caprice of Nature, does much to prevent over-crowding and inbreeding. Although male ground squirrels don't have harems, one adult can contribute more than his share to the birthrate by serving a number of females; thus a healthy population can be maintained with relatively few males.

Having built a heavy layer of fat during May and June, adult males retire for the winter in the first two weeks of July, and are followed by barren females in the next two weeks. In August and September, most of the colony above ground will consist of the young of the year, who need the extra days of growth so they can survive the eight-month hibernation and emerge as adults the next spring.

Because the bitter cold of a prairie winter can freeze the ground to a depth of more than 1 m, the hibernating chamber is invariably located off the deepest passage, and well insulated with dried vegetation. Before retiring, these ground squirrels carefully plug the passage to the sleeping chamber so that it appears to be another blind alley. This is a vital safety precaution; should they be discovered by a weasel or badger, they are absolutely helpless. Mr. H.H. Pittman described the vulnerability of ground squirrels during hibernation in an article for the *Canadian Geographical Journal* (November 1955).

In mid-winter they are rolled up in tight round balls with a temperature very slightly above that of the den and a heart-beat that is almost imperceptible. They appear to be dead. They may be rolled along the ground or used as a ball without awakening . . .

Although they store a generous supply of seeds and other food in their burrows, it is unlikely that any is eaten during the winter since Richardson's ground squirrels are thought to be profound hibernators. Instead, it probably serves as "emergency rations" when they emerge in March, at a time when snow covers most of their graze, and spring snowstorms can blanket the prairies without warning. Having woken from their sleep, they remain active regardless of the weather, and these rations can mean the difference between life and death.

Laboratory experiments by Drs. Gail and Daniel Michener of the University of Saskatchewan have proved that even after eight months of hibernation Richardson's ground squirrels are able to distinguish individual members of their family from other squirrels.

Natural Enemies

These little creatures have numerous enemies. Possibly the most dangerous are avian predators such as the Red-tailed Hawk, Swainson's Hawk, Rough-legged Hawk, Ferruginous Hawk, and Prairie Falcon. On land, they are no match for a fox or coyote in a footrace. Within their dens, they are preyed upon by weasels, ermine, Burrowing Owls, badgers, bull snakes, and rattlesnakes.

Relations with Humans

Man has upset the balance of Nature by killing off or seriously reducing the number of this rodent's natural enemies. As a result, Richardson's ground squirrels have extended their range and developed an appetite for farmers' crops, especially wheat and oats.

They are considered to be one of the most serious agricultural pests in Canada and have been under continual attack since the late-nineteenth century when bounties were offered in Manitoba. Extensive poisoning programmes have proven to be most effective, but other, more beneficial, species have been negatively affected also. Indeed, the attitude towards this ground squirrel is totally negative. I remember seeing men on a construction site near Regina gleefully chasing down these squirrels and clubbing them to death with sticks.

Much has been made of the fact that this species was the carrier of fleas bearing bubonic-plague germs. This is true, and at least one person died of the plague near Drumheller, Alberta, in 1937. In addition, Richardson's ground squirrels in the Medicine Hat, Alberta, area were identified as hosts of the *Dermacentor* tick that carries Rocky Mountain spotted fever. They are also occasionally known to carry Tularaemia bacteria.

This does not mean that these ground squirrels are an inordinate threat to humans. Almost all mammals are capable of carrying fatal diseases, including rabies, and the main carriers of tularaemia are the rabbit family, including the white-tailed jack rabbit, which occupies the same range as the Richardson's ground squirrel.

Rodent control is clearly justified to prevent crop damage and the spread of disease. However, since great decreases in Richardson's ground squirrel populations have been reported recently, we must obviously reassess our control programme lest we add yet another name to our ever-growing list of endangered species.

Where to Observe

This is one of the easiest animals to observe. Drive along any dirt road in the southern prairies, and watch for this ground squirrel's silhouette in the short grass—you may even spot one standing on the road.

Columbian Ground Squirrel
Spermophile du Columbia
Spermophilus columbianus

Common Names

In Canada, the Columbian ground squirrel is often known as a mountain gopher because of his shape and habitat; or a picket pin, because of his upright stance.

His scientific name, *Spermophilus columbianus*, is also descriptive; *Spermophilus* is Greek, meaning "lover of seeds", while *columbianus* is the Latinized place-name for part of his geographical range, the basin of the Columbia River.

Description

This plump ground squirrel has grey along the sides of his head, a tawny snout, and a pale eye-ring. His short coat appears beige at a distance, but the dense fur is speckled with buff and black on the back and sides. His underparts are a pale ginger, and his bushy brown tail has a light band near its tip. Key field-marks are his rufous legs and nose.

Adults of both sexes grow to an overall length of around 35 cm, and reach a peak weight in late summer of approximately 500 g.

Columbian Ground Squirrel

Canadian Range

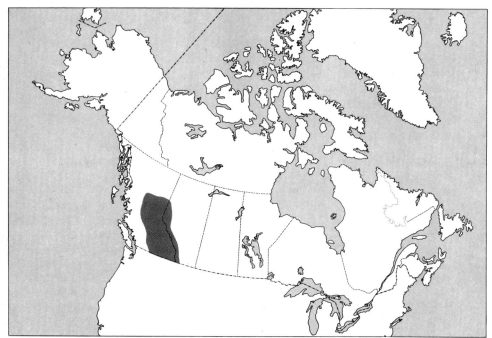

Range

Columbian ground squirrels live in the central Rocky Mountain regions of Alberta and British Columbia, at altitudes from 200 to 2600 m. Their kidney-shaped range stretches from the United States border in the south, to Wembley, Alberta, in the north; and from the foothills of the Rockies in Alberta, west to the Ashnola River in British Columbia.

Population density varies with the terrain, but in suitable habitat there may be from 10 to 20 adult squirrels per hectare.

Behaviour

Columbian ground squirrels live in colonies that are subdivided into territories. Each territory is controlled by a dominant male, and may include several adult females, plus yearlings and juveniles of both sexes.

Although the dominant male is a despot, his privileges of leadership are offset by the need to guard his territory against males from other communes. He is kept very busy. When he is not patrolling and marking his boundaries, breaking up scuffles among his offspring, or chasing away outsiders, he can usually be seen doing sentry duty on a promontory.

These alert little squirrels scurry from place to place in a series of bounds that are punctuated by flips of their tails. They are indifferent climbers and swimmers, but excellent leapers; Dr. André Steiner, a leading authority on ground-squirrel behaviour, once saw a Columbian jump a creek 2 m wide.

Members of this species are diurnal, emerging from their burrows shortly after sunup and retiring just before sunset. Most of their feeding is done in the forenoon; the rest of the day is spent sunbathing, playing, working on burrows, or taking a dustbath; the last activity culminates with a dramatic tail flourish that envelopes them in a tiny cloud of dust. In the late afternoon, there is a second but less-intense feeding period.

The most hectic time for social encounters is the three-week breeding season in May. During this period there are numerous hostile confrontations among the adult males, ranging from flank-to-flank shoving matches, which are more a test of strength than a fight, to vicious frontal attacks, during which deep bites are inflicted around the head and shoulders of the victim. In normal times, most encounters consist of tail fluffing and nose-to-nose greetings.

The most frequently heard call of Columbian ground squirrels is a short series of rasping chirps, which they utter standing on their hind legs; anyone approaching a colony is usually serenaded by a chorus of squirrels standing by their burrows like picket pins. However, when faced with an immediate threat such as a swooping hawk, they give a shrill whistle and disappear.

Personality

Dr. V. Keith Kivett, of the University of Alberta, wrote to me recently about a Columbian ground squirrel he had known:

It isn't often that one has an opportunity to develop a friendly relationship with a wild animal, but I was fortunate to have a male Columbian ground squirrel as a pet for six years. His curiosity and inquisitive nature earned him the name "Snooks", and his love for peanut butter was the reason I was able to lure him away from his littermates, the first day they ventured from their burrow.

Snooks quickly adjusted to daily human handling and became tolerant to the extent that he would gently nibble on your finger, (rather than biting hard), when he objected to an unpleasant situation.

As a youngster, Snooks enjoyed playing hide-and-seek, but his favourite game was rough-and-tumble wrestling. Often he would coax me into this game by pulling on my hand, and then he would pounce on my two outstretched fingers and hold on for dear life, with his forepaws and teeth, while I tried to shake him off.

As he grew older, Snooks became less playful, but his tameness and good nature were special assets for scent communication experiments in the laboratory. Columbian ground squirrels rub a gland (located near the corner of their mouth) on rocks and other convenient objects—other squirrels pick up these messages when they sniff the signposts. Whenever I dabbed the scent from another male in the room that Snooks considered his territory he would become excited, chatter his teeth, flare his tail; and look frantically around for the intruder. Then he would carefully rub his scent on every object in sight.

In his last year, even though age was taking its toll, Snooks became an instant "hit" on a nature television show. Throughout his long life Snooks' friendly and tolerant personality helped greatly in studying the behaviour of his species—in addition to being an unforgettable pleasure for me.

Habitat

Columbian ground squirrels like to take advantage of the sun by selecting a site with a southern exposure, and prefer to dig in porous soil because it is easy to excavate and provides natural drainage. During the course of the year, they may occupy three types of home: a nesting den, a summer burrow, and a hibernating den.

Because of the threat of marauding males, nesting dens are usually located close to the centre of the territory. They are simply constructed, consisting of a single chamber, a spoil room, and two or three auxiliary entrances.

Summer burrows are located conveniently near the main food source. They consist of a prominent front entrance and many concealed auxiliary entrances or bolt holes that are connected to the core by a network of shallow passages. These underground passages reduce the risk of being caught in the open by a predator when the squirrels make their daily feeding sorties.

Hibernating dens are the deepest type of burrow, the depth being limited chiefly by the level of hardpan or bedrock; most are from 1 to 2 m below ground. Often these dens are dug into the side of a slope, and the sleeping chamber is sited above the entrance level so that water will not collect in the nest. Hibernating dens sited in flat meadows or at the edge of grainfields are subject to severe flooding, but these little rodents solve the problem ingeniously by digging a vertical passage from their sleeping chamber, which acts as a sump hole to drain off any water that might flood the chamber.

Feeding Habits

Columbian ground squirrels are omnivores who prefer vegetation, but they sometimes eat mice, and they can snatch a grasshopper out of the air with the dexterity of a baseball player trapping a line drive.

Most of their feeding takes place during the morning, and like raccoons, they fastidiously clean their paws after each meal. Early in the year they concentrate on the roots and stalks of plants; when the buds burst, they switch to leaves and fresh shoots; late in the season they savour flowers and fruit. Staples in their diet include the bulbs of wild onions and glacier lilies; the leaves and flowers of strawberry, dandelion, ragweed, and buttercup plants; and gooseberries, currants, and serviceberries.

Prior to hibernation, most males transfer cheekloads of grain and rot-resistant seeds to their winter dens. This cache can be a boon the following spring, but often attracts their less-provident brothers, who don't hesitate to filch a free meal.

Breeding takes place in the three weeks following emergence, and is marked by fighting and aggressive behaviour among the males.

Gestation for this species is normally 24 days, with the average litter being 4 pups. At birth, the blind and hairless infants weigh only 9 g, but like most ground squirrels, they grow rapidly. The pups are weaned shortly after they emerge from the natal den, at the age of 4 weeks; those who persist in suckling receive a slap on the nose from their mother. Some extremely adventurous youngsters may choose this time to leave the burrow and dig a simple den for themselves.

Life Cycle

Throughout most of their Canadian range, male Columbian ground squirrels emerge from hibernation in the last part of April, and are joined by the females and yearlings at the beginning of May. These dates vary depending on the latitude and the severity of the winter.

Young Columbians love to play. Most games start when one teases the other, or makes a sudden pounce; this develops into wrestling matches or chases, the latter often spiced with acrobatics, including somersaults, and their version of leap-frog. These encounters simulate adult clashes in that there are dominant and subordinate players, as well as appropriate sound effects such as growling, chattering, and teeth gnashing.

By late summer juveniles weigh around 250 g but they do not attain full maturity until they are two years old, even though the males will probably disperse as yearlings. Since they are slow to mature, they are relatively long-lived, with a life expectancy in the wild of 4 to 6 years.

In a normal year, adult Columbian ground squirrels hibernate around the end of August. However, exceptionally dry weather in July may induce them to enter their dens early. Yearlings and juveniles need extra feeding time, and sometimes stay above ground well into September.

Mature animals excavate deeply, to get as much protection from the elements and predators as possible; and they site their dens on a slope, or dig a sump hole, to ensure good drainage. Immature squirrels usually dig shallow burrows, and are more casual in their approach to the problem of drainage. For these reasons, winter mortality is higher among the young, who contribute more than their share to the annual loss, which may range from 40 to 55 per cent of the total population.

Having selected their burrows, these squirrels line their sleeping chambers with grass, and partially excavate an exit passage in the ceiling. The spoil from the exit passage is then used to plug the entrance tunnel to hibernation chambers. Once everything is in order, they curl up sitting on their tail, with their nose pressed against their belly, and remain in that position for the next 7 months.

Natural Enemies

Columbian ground squirrels are preyed upon by foxes, weasels, badgers, skunks, wolves, and coyotes. In the autumn, when the vegetation dies, grizzly bears spend a significant amount of effort digging these little hibernators out of their dens. During the summer, buteo hawks and Golden Eagles are a constant threat from the sky.

Relations with Humans

Because the land is sparsely settled throughout this ground squirrel's Canadian range, and since much of it is unsuitable for farming, Man has had little influence.

This species has no direct economic value, but as well as being an engaging sight for hikers and campers, it is an important link in the food chain of a number of carnivores who are valuable furbearers.

Like many other mammals, the Columbian ground squirrel occasionally hosts the *Dermacentor* tick that transmits Rocky Mountain spotted fever.

Columbian ground squirrels enjoy vegetable-garden produce, and will happily feed in a grainfield all summer. However, few of their colonies are in close proximity to civilization, and they are not considered to be a serious pest.

Where to Observe

Columbian ground squirrels are found in a wide variety of terrain, and frequently reveal themselves by their chattering. Often they are quite tame, and a handful of peanuts will frequently lure them into close camera-range.

Arctic Ground Squirrel
Spermophile arctique
Spermophilus parryii

Common Names
His universal nickname, given to him many years ago by the Eskimos, is "Sik Sik", which needs no translation as it is simply the sound of his chattering call.

His scientific name, *Spermophilus parryii*, is a combination of Greek and Latin: *Spermophilus* means "lover of seeds", while *parryii* is the Latinized name of a famous Arctic explorer, Sir William Parry. However, Sir William was not the discoverer of this species; it was named in his honour by a contemporary, Sir John Richardson, in 1825.

Description
From a distance an arctic ground squirrel appears to be beige; at close range he has a lot of tan in his coat, which is relieved by a white eye-ring, diffused white spots on his back, and a dark brushy tail. His underparts are putty-coloured. This species moults twice during the summer; because of the short time-span, his pelt is usually in a transitional phase. The spring moult starts at his rump and progresses to his head, while the autumn moult, which is paler, goes in the opposite direction.

Both sexes attain an overall length of approximately 39 cm, which makes them the largest of the ground squirrels. Males average around 800 g, while females average 700 g.

Arctic Ground Squirrel

Canadian Range

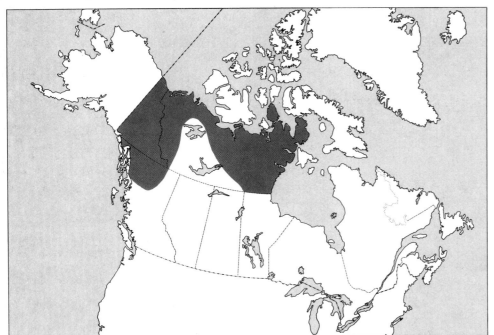

Range
Arctic ground squirrels are found from the Arctic Circle to the southern border of the Northwest Territories, in a 3000 km swath that stretches from the west coast of Hudson Bay to the coast of British Columbia, at altitudes from sea level to 900 m.

This species lives in colonies that may host from 5 to 50 animals depending on the suitability of the habitat.

Behaviour

Arctic ground squirrels are influenced by two unusual environmental factors. One is the continuous daylight during summer; since they are diurnal, one would suppose they would be active round the clock. However, this is not so; even in the brightest phase they maintain a "normal" schedule, and retire to their dens for about eight hours each night.

The other factor is the lack of cover in their habitat, which combined with their wide-ranging nature (it is not uncommon for a squirrel to make a straight-line journey of more than a kilometre), would appear to expose them to undue risk. To compensate for the lack of cover, they move with their bodies pressed close to the ground in a manner aptly described as the "tundra glide".

This species lives in scattered colonies that are subdivided into territories under the control of a dominant male. Each territory is occupied by one or more adult females. This social system differs from a coterie or a harem in that females share a common piece of property. The dominant male of each territory prevents other males from moving into his personal bailiwick.

Dominant males mark their boundaries by rubbing surfaces with scent from glands in their cheeks and back. Social encounters may involve nose-to-nose contact or pressing against each other in a variety of postures—one of the most common is flank to flank. Pressing against each other is more of a test than a display of affection, and often leads to a shoving match that can deteriorate into a chase or violent scuffle. Fights are short, but the contestants, who often end up rolling about in a ball, use both teeth and claws, and many males suffer severe wounds.

The chattering "sik sik" call of these rodents can be heard for long distances over the treeless tundra. When chattering, they stand on their hind legs and make the sound with an open mouth, exposing their tongue—rather like a Bronx cheer. However, if the danger is close at hand, they prudently refrain from making a sound until they reach the safety of their den or similar cover. An American naturalist, Herbert V. Melchior, studied their calls over a period of years and came to the conclusion that these squirrels use a gutteral chatter for land-borne enemies, and a short, narrow-band whistle for avian predators. Because hawks and owls have excellent direction-sensing ability with wide-band sounds, the short narrow-band whistle has the twin advantages of being quick to utter and difficult to pinpoint. By employing two distinct alarm signals, "sik siks" know what to expect and can act accordingly. Dr. Melchior wrote of an instance when a Rough-legged Hawk flew over a colony and landed near three squirrels; while the hawk was airborne they gave the whistle alert, when it landed they switched to the chatter, and when it took wing again they whistled it out of sight.

Young ground squirrels suffer high mortality in their first year from a number of causes. One hazard is the likelihood of the dominant male raiding their den and killing them. Another danger, because of their inexperience, lies in their choice of a hibernating den that may be badly insulated or subject to flooding. A third risk is the likelihood of being caught by a predator when they disperse from their birth site in late summer. Although many juveniles die during dispersal, the phase is ultimately beneficial to the species because it prevents inbreeding, and reduces pressure on the slow-growing food supply.

Personality

Fred Bruemmer, the noted Canadian journalist and photographer, wrote in his book *Encounters with Arctic Animals: One day I met a very fat male siksik. He dashed off in a porcine gallop, bobbing his bulbous little buttocks, and shot underneath a big flat stone. "Aha", I thought, "now I've got you!" I spent a good hour barricading with rocks every possible exit but one, while the siksik below commented on my labors with a steady stream of raucous invective. I set up the camera and focussed it on the only hole left open, sure now to get some pictures. For a while the siksik kept up his muffled maledictions; then it became very quiet. I waited and waited, and suddenly I saw the siksik. He had somehow squeezed out, and was now behind me busily nibbling at my camera bag!*

Habitat

The arctic ground squirrel's principal habitat is the Arctic tundra, in areas that are well vegetated and not too wet. Permafrost (permanently frozen subsoil with the consistency of concrete) has a major influence on his choice of location. Because water is the binding agent for permafrost, this ground squirrel can only dig in porous sand or gravel, and he must site his dens on well-drained ridges or banks. In the southern part of his range he frequently lives in open meadows. Because of the permafrost problem, burrows are seldom more than 1 m deep. Most squirrels use two types of burrow: a single but elaborate "home" burrow, and several "bachelor" burrows.

A typical home burrow is an extraordinary maze of tunnels on different levels, which includes one or more sleeping chambers, a number of spoil rooms, and numerous openings. Bachelor burrows are located near the home burrow and are used sporadically as an emergency refuge or place to spend the night; normally they simply consist of a short tunnel, and lack the amenities of a home burrow.

Feeding Habits

This rodent is primarily herbivorous, although it is said with justification that he will eat almost anything—including his own kind. Normally he feeds on the roots, stalks, leaves, flowers, seeds, and berries of a variety of plants. His main feeding activity takes place in the forenoon; he forages rapidly, moving from patch to patch with brief stops to sit up and check for danger. Usually he cuts the vegetation with his teeth and then holds it in both paws to eat it. He will also stuff his cheeks with leaves or seeds and carry them back to his den for later consumption; this cargo is sometimes topped off with a mouthful of grass to line his nest. Among his favourite foods are: grasses, sedges, mushrooms, bog rushes, bilberries, and willows.

Life Cycle

The first to emerge from hibernation in mid-April or early May, depending upon the latitude, are the males, who are joined a week later by the females. Breeding takes place during May and the young are born in June after a 25-day gestation period. Litter size ranges from 5 to 10 pups, who are born blind and hairless, weighing approximately 10 g. Fortunately, the tiny infants grow rapidly, for they have less than 5 months before winter sets in; when they are weaned at 6 weeks they have a dense, well-dappled coat, and weigh around 500 g.

Throughout the summer, adult ground squirrels spend most of their day feeding or loafing in the sun. Grooming is part of their daily routine and often includes a dustbath. By the end of August, most adults have acquired a heavy layer of fat, which will be used to fuel their metabolism during the winter.

Adult females retire to their hibernating chambers early in September, and are closely followed by the adult males. The young of the year remain active until the end of September or the beginning of October; they need this extra time to attain maximum growth before hibernation. Sometimes, when the young are ready to hibernate, they find that most of the suitable dens are occupied. When this situation occurs, a cold snap can force them into unfavourable sites where they perish. If they survive their first winter, they will be fully mature the following spring.

Prior to sealing themselves in their hibernation chamber, which measures approximately 36 cm in diameter, and 28 cm in height, arctic ground squirrels lay in a store of food. The amount of food cached varies with the availability of seeds, although male squirrels usually cache considerably more than females. This reserve is eaten during their periods of arousal through the winter, and is also used to augment their food supply when they first emerge in the spring, a time when the vegetation is sparse and frequently hidden by snow.

Experienced animals select a burrow in well-drained ground and occupy a sleeping chamber deep in the labyrinth of tunnels. This type of site is not likely to be flooded, and provides maximum insulation as well as protection against marauding bears. In preparation for the long winter, they make a nest composed of dried grass, leaves, and bits of caribou fur collected on the tundra. When they are snug in their nests, they curl into a ball, (sitting on their haunches), with their head between their legs, flip their tail over their head like a cape, and slip into sleep.

Hibernation lasts for approximately seven months. During the course of a winter it is not unusual for individual animals, particularly females and juveniles, to lose 30 or 40 per cent of their body weight; thus hibernation can be a severe test.

Natural Enemies

Arctic ground squirrels are a staple food for the grizzly bear during early spring and late autumn when fresh greens are unavailable. The grizzly is capable of digging them out of their shallow dens in the tundra, and will often systematically clear the overburden from a burrow until he locates the squirrels in their sleeping chambers. Throughout the summer, arctic and red foxes, wolves, and ermine also take a toll. Airborne predators include the Rough-legged Hawk, Peregrine Falcon, Gyrfalcon, and Snowy Owl.

Relations with Humans

Because of the remoteness of this ground squirrel's habitat, Man has had relatively little influence on the species. However, with the opening of the North, this situation could change, and it is to be hoped that this harmless and attractive little creature will not suffer as a result.

In the past, the arctic ground squirrel provided both food and clothing for the people of the North. Today, it continues to be of economic value because it is a major food source for a number of important furbearers including ermine, foxes, bears, and wolves.

Where to Observe

Although some zoos have this ground squirrel, the best place to observe him is in his natural habitat. He is not difficult to find, and it is likely he will see you first and announce his presence with a loud chattering call. He is very tame, and should you be camping nearby, he will probably visit you for handouts.

Thirteen-lined Ground Squirrel
Spermophile rayé
Spermophilus tridecemlineatus

Common Names
His most popular nicknames, striped gopher and striped ground squirrel, refer to his ribbon-like markings. Since the turn of the century, youngsters in the Prairie Provinces have shortened these titles to striper or stripey.

His long scientific name, *Spermophilus tridecemlineatus*, makes excellent sense once it is translated from the Greek and Latin. *Spermophilus* means "lover of seeds", while *tridecemlineatus* means "thirteen lined".

Description
This slender squirrel may be easily mistaken for a surveyor's stake in an overgrown field. At close range, he is immediately recognizable because of his distinctive coat: along his back and sides are seven brown stripes with buff spots, separated by six beige stripes. The pattern is less clear on the crown of his head; his nose and cheeks are cinnamon, and he has a pale eye-ring. His legs and the underparts of his body are a ginger shade, while his tail has a mixture of colours that produce a dark-mustard tone.

Thirteen-lined ground squirrels moult twice each year. Their spring fur appears near the head and grows toward the tail; their autumn coat is the reverse. Adult males attain an average length of 28 cm, and weigh around 200 g by late summer. Females are slightly smaller, with an average length of 26 cm, and a peak weight of about 180 g.

Thirteen~lined Ground Squirrel

Canadian Range

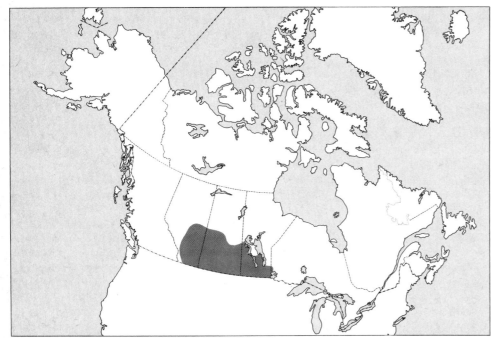

Range

The Central Plains region of the Prairie Provinces is the northern tip of his continental range, which stretches all to the way to the Gulf of Mexico. In Canada, he is found in the southern portions of Manitoba, Saskatchewan, and Alberta.

In 1939, a single male thirteen-lined ground squirrel was discovered near Quebec City and forwarded to the National Museum for identification. Both Dr. R.M. Anderson of the National Museum and Dr. R. Bernard of the Jardin Zoologique agreed that this individual probably migrated via the CNR as the pet of a western tourist rather than on foot.

Population density in Canada is approximately 5 squirrels to the hectare, but in the central United States, there may be as many as 50 to the hectare.

Behaviour

Thirteen-lined ground squirrels live alone or in small family groups. When a number of these rodents dig burrows in close proximity to each other, it is because of the appeal of the habitat, rather than a desire to be sociable. Since they are relatively indifferent to their neighbours, most agonistic behaviour takes place during the breeding season, and the loser rarely suffers more than a few nips on the flank. Once the mating is over, the males tend to ignore each other.

This species is diurnal, with the peak period of activity running from mid-morning to late afternoon; if the weather is wet or windy, they remain in their dens. Home territory or range varies according to the terrain; however, males usually cover more ground than females, and in open country may utilize up to 4 ha.

These squirrels are wary by nature and prefer to be hidden by foliage when moving from place to place. At the first hint of danger, they make for the nearest hole; if they are prevented from going to ground, they freeze with their belly pressed to the earth. Although their coat has prominent markings, the dappled pattern breaks their outline and they blend beautifully with the surroundings.

Like the other ground squirrels, they frequently assume an upright "picket-pin" stance to get a better view of an area. To gain additional height, they often stand with their hind legs fully extended, and it is in this position that they look like a surveyor's stake because they seem so long and thin (their tail, which is used as a brace, is hidden by the grass).

They have little difficulty in climbing low bushes, and are strong swimmers; Dr. Stuart Criddle wrote in the *Canadian Field-Naturalist* (January 1939) of several that swam the Assiniboine River during high water, at a spot where the banks were more than 80 m apart.

They have a variety of calls, the most noteworthy being the short, sharp, alarm whistle, and a bubbling bird-like trill that they use frequently throughout the day. The trill is quite extraordinary because they can "throw" the notes like a ventriloquist, making it extremely difficult for humans to locate them. When infant ground squirrels become separated from their mother, they make a peeping sound every few seconds that permits her to collect them systematically. Unfortunately, she is unable to count, and if a stray fails to make the peeping signal, it is overlooked.

Because of the ever-present ticks, mites, and fleas, these ground squirrels spend a lot of time grooming themselves. The final procedure is to clean their tail, which they do by drawing it through their mouth from base to tip, and then giving it a flick to get the hairs in place.

Personality

Ernest Thompson Seton wrote about this species in his *Lives of Game Animals*, using the nickname, Flag Citelle:

. . . if you find a Flag Citelle sitting by its burrow, and walk straight toward it, it waits till you are within perhaps ten feet, then dives with a little defiant chirrup into its underground safety. If you walk so far as to pass within eight or ten feet, and do not look at it, it seems to watch your eye, and remains perfectly still while you pass. If you step or turn toward it, it dives at once.

If on the prairies the creature be followed, not too fast, it will play with the observer, leading him about in various directions, without seeking a hole. I remember once (July 16, 1892) following one for a hundred yards or more in a very crooked course; then, so far from hieing earthward at last, it took to a field of standing wheat and eluded me in that, giving the usual chuckle of defiance as it disappeared.

If, however, it be hotly pursued, it makes for its earthworks shelter. . . . But possessed of an uncontrollable curiosity, it is sure to peep out again if all be still; and it is easily taken then in a noose laid over the hole where it first disappeared.

Habitat

Thirteen-lined ground squirrels live in the transitional belt between grassland and forest, which is characterized by low ground-cover. Because of their need to dig a deep burrow, the choice of soil is critical. Favourite haunts are overgrown meadows or the scrubby margins of sloughs and streams. They are also found in stands of aspen, the lightly wooded edges of forests, small swales on the prairies, and close to farmers' fields.

Thirteen-lined ground squirrels inhabit two types of burrow during the year. One is used as a feeding station, while the other is their "home" or hibernating den. The chief difference between the two is the depth, as both have a sleeping chamber and a labyrinth of tunnels leading to store rooms. Summer burrows are usually less than 30 cm below the surface; "home" burrows are often excavated to a depth of 2 m. More than one squirrel may use a given burrow, but only one will occupy it at a time. Occasionally this species will take up residence in a vacant Richardson's ground-squirrel den.

To avoid detection by predators, these squirrels remove all traces of soil at the main entrance and bolt holes by scattering the earth with their hind feet. "Home" burrows are cleverly engineered to foil one of their chief enemies, the badger. Since badgers must have a clear backspace to throw the earth when they dig, the squirrels put an L-shaped bend in the tunnel leading to the sleeping chamber. It doesn't always work, but it is a deterrent in some instances. Before retiring, they usually take the precaution of blocking the entrances to their dens with plugs of earth or grass.

Feeding Habits

It is fortunate that this little squirrel is quick on his feet and adept with his paws, because he needs all his faculties to satisfy his omnivorous appetite. In addition to eating a wide range of vegetation, he consumes a substantial amount of animal matter including insects, grasshoppers, beetles, caterpillars, mice, the eggs and young of birds—even the occasional small snake.

In the early spring, ground squirrels concentrate on roots, seeds, and green shoots. When the insects emerge, these rodents become strongly carnivorous, to the extent that animal material may compose more than half their daily intake. Late in the summer they shift back to a vegetable diet, paying particular attention to the ripening fruit bushes. During this season they are frequently observed, their cheek pouches bulging with booty, making countless trips from the fields as they stock the larder of their burrows with seeds and grain.

Life Cycle

In the Prairie Provinces, male thirteen-lined ground squirrels emerge from hibernation early in April and are joined by the females later in the month. Mating takes place over the next few weeks, and the young are born at the end of May or the beginning of June after a gestation period of 28 days. The average size of a litter is 8. The pups, who are blind and hairless, weigh only 6 g but grow very quickly. When they are weaned at 4 weeks they weigh 70 g, and are exceedingly mobile.

Although ground-squirrel mothers lose interest in their offspring soon after they are weaned, they are very protective of their babies for the first few days above ground. In the southern part of the range, should a mother lose her first litter because of flooding or predators, she will likely breed again and bear a second family later in the summer.

Most litters disperse two weeks after they emerge from the natal den. Young males travel up to 700 m before digging their own shallow burrows, while juvenile females stay closer to home.

Adult males begin hibernating at the end of September; juveniles, and females who have had litters, continue feeding into October. All are in their dens by the beginning of November. The survival rate for this species varies dramatically from year to year; the normal loss is from 5 to 50 per cent of the population. Like humans, female ground squirrels are usually longer-lived than males. Juveniles who survive the winter are fully mature the following spring.

During the last weeks of summer, thirteen-lined ground squirrels stock their hibernaculum with nonperishable seeds—as many as 2,000 kernels of wheat have been counted—and line their sleeping chambers with grass. When collecting grass for their nest, they sometimes stuff their mouth so full that the bundle almost obscures them from view, and the stalks dragging along the ground impede their progress. By this time they are very fat, and the preparations must be quite a chore. Indeed, in the days just prior to hibernation, they become increasingly listless, foraging close to their dens, or just sitting with their head and shoulders protruding from the hole.

When they finally retire to their chambers, which are approximately 20 cm in diameter, they carefully plug all the entrances with earth. For the next 6 months they remain curled in a loop with their head between their hind legs, except for brief periods when they wake for a few hours to eat and perform body functions.

Upon emerging in the spring, they are somewhat disoriented and spend the first days close to their den. It is at this stage that their cache of food becomes vital; by winter's end they have lost up to 50 per cent of their body weight, and the vegetation is sparse.

Natural Enemies

This species is vulnerable to airborne attacks from buteo hawks, and infant ground squirrels are often killed by crows. Foxes and coyotes take their toll above ground, while weasels and badgers threaten the safety of the dens.

Thirteen-lined ground squirrels are bothered by fleas, mites, and ticks. However, the worst parasites are the larvae of the botfly (*Cuterebra*), which frequently lodge in the groin. These grubs can grow to a length of 2.5 cm—by human comparison, the size of a football—and can seriously impair the squirrel's health.

Relations with Humans

On one hand we have reduced the number of this species' natural enemies; on the other hand we have employed traps, guns, and poison—plus a bounty in some areas—to eradicate these squirrels whenever they come in contact with us.

The thirteen-lined ground squirrel can be a pest in the early summer to farmers and vegetable gardeners. In addition, he is regarded as a nuisance on golf courses—a charge that adds insult to injury, because the large holes attributed to him are made by badgers when they dig these little creatures out of their homes.

In considering the damage caused by this rodent, we should remember that he eats an enormous amount of grasshoppers and other harmful insects, as well as mice. Most authorities agree that he does as much good as he does harm, and should therefore be left alone.

Where to Observe

The thirteen-lined ground squirrel tries to remain out of sight whenever possible. For this reason the best way to locate one is to listen for his bird-like trill. Should you frighten him into his burrow don't despair; in a minute or two his curiosity will compel him to pop up for another look at you.

Franklin's Ground Squirrel
Spermophile de Franklin
Spermophilus franklinii

Common Names

Because of his clear, tremulous call, which Ernest Thompson Seton described as being "in a high degree musical, resembling the voices of some of our fine bird singers", he is often known as the whistling ground squirrel. Other common nicknames, because of his resemblance to the Richardson's ground squirrel, are bush gopher and grey gopher.

His scientific name, *Spermophilus franklinii*, is a combination of Greek and Latin; *Spermophilus* means "lover of seeds", while *franklinii* is the Latinized surname of Sir John Franklin. Sir John Richardson discovered this species in 1821 near Carlton House, Saskatchewan, while he was attached to Sir John Franklin's expedition to find the Northwest Passage, and he named it in honour of his leader.

Description

The Franklin's ground squirrel is as trimly shaped as a tree squirrel, and appears at a distance to be grey in colour. At close range, his coat is tan, rippled with buff and black bars, and his underparts are a light ginger. His head is grey, with a white eye-ring, and the hairs on his long, brown, bushy tail are tipped with silver.

The average length for both sexes is approximately 38 cm, although the males, which weigh around 475 g, are slightly heavier than the females, which weigh approximately 425 g.

Franklin's Ground Squirrel

Canadian Range

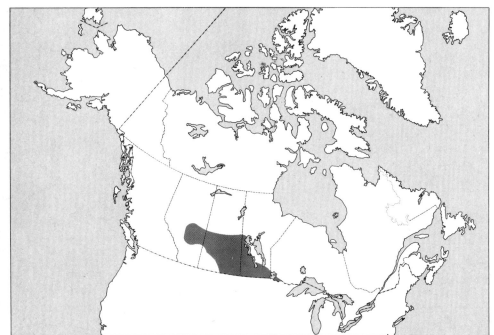

Range

This ground squirrel is found in an irregular belt stretching from the Rainy River area of western Ontario, through to Edmonton, Alberta. Population densities fluctuate radically depending upon food availability; thus, suitable terrain may host up to 12 adults to the hectare one year and none the next year. In addition, these ground squirrels are selective in their choice of habitat, often leaving large tracts within their range barren.

Behaviour

Franklin's ground squirrels are considered to be colonial, but most live in small family groups, or alone, rather than in large communities. Although they are diurnal, they spend much of their life underground, partly because of their secretive nature, but also because of their sensitivity to inclement weather—they don't like precipitation, high winds, or unseasonable temperatures.

During their active periods, they are very frisky, and it is not unusual to see them darting through the branches of low trees or berry bushes; when faced with the necessity, they are excellent swimmers. Normally, they live in an area with thick ground-cover and follow sheltered paths, which radiate from their burrows to feeding areas. Thus, it is difficult for humans and predators to spot these ground squirrels unless they listen for the bird-like whistle, and stealthily track it to its source. This rodent is quick to take alarm and disappear into his den, but his inquisitive nature is frequently his undoing, because he can't resist the temptation to put his head out of his hole to check on the intruder.

Personality

G.L. Saunders, in the *Victoria Naturalist* (January 1966) wrote of an amusing association with a Franklin's ground squirrel:

We shall never know how a bush gopher came to set up house under the cabin of a summer camp on an island in northern Saskatchewan, but there he was: he was first, and he was staying. Someone christened him John Willie, and everyone loved him. That first summer he had it all his own way; he got so bold he would come into the cabin and search the table, the cupboards, and our pockets for food. Soon he was eating from the cats' dish to their obvious disgust.

Often out in the woods we would hear a rustling among the dry leaves and a high-pitched "Willy, Willy, Willy" would bring him scampering. Of course we had to produce something edible: a nut, a raisin, a cutworm. But not a pentatomid stink bug; I tried that on him once, and was he insulted! Like all northern districts, the place swarmed with mosquitoes which we fought with smoke and dope and nets, but Willie would let a mosquito gorge on the end of his nose and never lift a paw.

When camp was broken at the beginning of September, John Willie was sleek and fat, and no doubt had a most unusual store of provender down in that hole. It was a glorious fall and we came back for the Thanksgiving week-end, but no Willie was in evidence; he must have gone into hibernation some time in September in spite of the mild weather.

The following summer, Dr. Saunders was surprised to find that several other adult Franklin's ground squirrels had come to the island—and even more surprised when John Willie gave birth to a litter of five little "Willies"!

Habitat

These squirrels favour the borderland or "transition zone" between the high coniferous forests and the open plains. This type of terrain, consisting of aspen stands and alders or other low trees, also has dense ground cover that can reach a height of 2 m. Undoubtedly the thick understory shelters them from the eyes of many predators, particularly the buteo hawks.

Typical burrow sites include ridges of high ground covered with scrub trees, the edges of lakes or marshes, and aspen bluffs adjacent to farms.

Burrows are usually sited on a ridge or bank to ensure good drainage. A typical burrow has an obvious main entrance with a prominent deposit of soil, and several craftily concealed auxiliary entrances that serve as bolt holes.

Because permafrost is not a problem in this ground squirrel's range, tunnelling is quite deep, with passages leading to one or more sleeping chambers, spoil rooms, and storage rooms. Because of the undergrowth, it is sometimes difficult to spot the burrows.

Feeding Habits

Franklin's ground squirrels are omnivores, whose diet may consist of up to 25 per cent animal matter such as mice, frogs, grasshoppers, small songbirds, and the eggs and young of wild ducks and poultry.

Most of their feeding takes place within a 100 m radius of their burrow, along well-worn trails leading from the main entrance. They are versatile food gatherers, who use their paws not only to dig up roots and to bend down grain stalks, but also to manipulate large unwieldy trophys such as a duck's egg, or a toad. Early in the spring, they feed on roots, grass sprouts, dandelion, and clover; as the summer progresses, they switch to thistles, nettles, and flowering plants. When fruit ripens, they eagerly climb elderberry and chokecherry bushes, relishing both the berries and the stones. If they live near a farm, they will make inroads in the sprouting corn, carrots, potatoes, peas, lettuce, and string beans. In this connection, laboratory tests indicate that these rodents, who will eat most anything, have little appetite for onions, peppers, or rhubarb.

Prior to hibernation, they store a considerable amount of vegetable matter, such as seeds, grain, fruit stones, and leaves, in their burrow to be consumed in the first days following emergence.

Life Cycle

Males emerge from hibernation in late April or early May, and are followed a week or so later by the females. Unlike many of their cousins, the sex ratio of adult Franklin's ground squirrels is one to one, rather than a plurality of females. This means that during the three-week breeding season, males must compete for a mate; there is constant scrapping, and many suffer severe bites on their hindquarters. However, beating off rival suitors is only half the battle; the conquest of a female is a rough-and-tumble affair, which is invariably preceded by a spirited chase.

Pregnant females line their natal den with grass and, after a gestation period of approximately 28 days, bear a litter of from 2 to 12 pups, the average being 8. At birth, the infants are blind and hairless, weighing approximately 9 g. Fortunately, they grow exceedingly fast; at three weeks they are fully furred; at four weeks they are scampering around the den; and at five weeks, when they are weaned, they weigh more than 200 g.

Social life in a Franklin's colony settles down after the breeding period, and feeding takes priority for the balance of the summer. Even after the emergence of the young in late June, there is little agonistic behaviour on the part of the adults, although the pups spend a lot of their time in competitive play.

Adult males start hibernating in July; a few weeks later the females also retire for the winter. By mid-August the young of the year are the only ones still above ground; they seek their dens in September. Juveniles who survive the winter will be fully mature the following spring, and may breed or disperse at that time.

Franklin's ground squirrels prepare for hibernation carefully. In addition to accumulating a thick layer of body fat and caching a generous reserve of food, they make sure that their hibernaculum is well sited and that their sleeping chamber is warmly lined with grass.

Despite these precautions, the mortality rate over the winter ranges from 40 to 80 per cent of the total population. Although one would expect the young of the year to account for most of the toll, the death rate is fairly evenly distributed among adults of both sexes and juveniles. Those that make it through the winter lose nearly half their body weight in the process.

Natural Enemies

On land, this species is preyed upon by the weasel, red fox, ermine, coyote, badger, and skunk. The buteo hawks, such as the Rough-legged, Ferruginous, Red-tailed, and Swainson's hawks, are the main threat from the air.

Although these squirrels have an impressive list of foes, predators are not considered to have a significant influence on the overall population. Part of the reason is that it is not worth the effort of most predators to hunt this rodent seriously because the colonies are small and individual members spend most of their life below ground.

Parasites and disease are their most devastating enemies; whenever there is a periodic increase in a colony of ground squirrels, these twin scourges reduce their numbers the following year.

Relations with Humans

Many people consider the Franklin's ground squirrel a pest. For this reason, he has been subjected to a long-standing programme designed to reduce his numbers, including shooting, trapping, and poisoning.

Although the Franklin's ground squirrel is an attractive little creature, he has earned a bad reputation with the farming community. On occasion these rodents will eat grain, pillage vegetable gardens, and raid henhouses.

An extensive research programme on the Delta Marsh in Manitoba, also known as the "Duck Factory" to sportsmen, revealed that the Franklin's ground squirrel ranked next to the Common Crow as a major predator of waterfowl. However, the researchers came to the conclusion that this animal was only a problem during times when it was abundant, and even then its depredations were restricted to certain localities. The recommendation of the research report was that control of the species should be left to Nature; disease and parasites would cut back the population as soon as there was a periodic upswing.

This natural solution has worked well on the Delta Marsh, and merits serious consideration whenever these squirrels become a nuisance.

Where to Observe

The Franklin's ground squirrel can be shy and secretive, and its colonies are widely scattered throughout its range. The best way to locate one is to listen for its musical whistle, and then quietly follow it to the source. In Alberta, they are easily seen around the picnic areas in some of the provincial parks, where they become very tame.

Golden-mantled Ground Squirrel
Spermophile à mante dorée
Spermophilus lateralis

Common Names

He is often called a golden chipmunk, or yellow head, because of his distinctive colour scheme; sometimes he is called a rock squirrel because of his habitat. In the United States, he is also known as Say's chipmunk in memory of Thomas Say who first identified the species in 1823.

This little ground squirrel has a lyrical scientific name, *Spermophilus lateralis; Spermophilus* is a Greek word meaning "lover of seeds", while *lateralis* is Latin for "of the side", and refers to the prominent stripe on each side of his body.

Description

At a distance, the golden-mantled ground squirrel resembles a large chipmunk. However, closer inspection reveals that his black-edged lateral stripes begin at his shoulders, rather than his cheeks, and he has a "mantle" of tawny fur covering his head, chest, and forepaws. His underparts are buff, while his back and flanks are grey, and his tail is brown.

The average length for this species is 29 cm, and the peak weight for both sexes is around 275 g.

Golden-mantled Ground Squirrel

Canadian Range

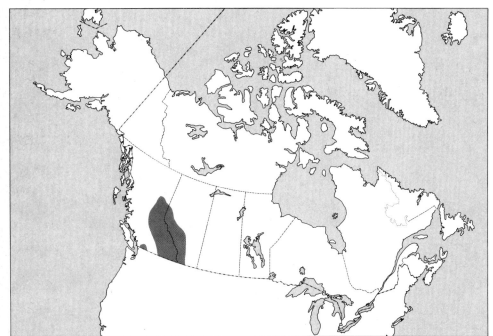

Range

The Canadian range of the golden-mantled ground squirrel is the central Rocky Mountains region of southern Alberta and British Columbia, at altitudes from 1600 to 2600 m. This ground squirrel's range is similar to that of the Columbian ground squirrel. Both species overlap, but the golden-mantled favours higher, more rocky ground, often living above tree-line in the mountains, and he avoids thick ground-cover.

Population density varies with the terrain, and some areas are barren. Suitable habitat may hold from 6 to 12 adult squirrels to the hectare.

Behaviour

Individual golden-mantled ground squirrels are highly independent, and are primarily concerned with their own welfare. They have no communal ties and their family life ends shortly after they emerge from the natal den. At that time their mother loses interest in them and may become actively hostile. The main bond shared by these rodents is their understanding and response to warning calls. When danger is sighted, one will give a few sharp chirps or make a chittering noise, accompanied by spasmodic twitches of the tail, and those within earshot heed the signal.

Although they are antisocial by nature, a special attraction such as a campground will draw them together like a magnet. When a crowd of these squirrels gathers, it is normal for the aggressive ones to get more than their fair share of the booty.

They have a strong hoarding instinct, and instead of consuming titbits on the spot, they will often stuff their cheek pouches until they bulge, and then scurry away and hide the loot in their dens or bury it in a shallow hole for later retrieval. One golden-mantled ground squirrel accepted nearly 2 kg of peanuts during the course of a day. He could only carry 3 peanuts at a time, and he was 100 m from his den, but he kept making round trips until the bag was empty!

These squirrels are diurnal and enjoy a good sunbath, except on the hottest days when they seek the shade of their dens from midmorning until late afternoon. In cold weather, they reverse this schedule by rising after 9 a.m. and retiring around 4 p.m. Heavy rain or high winds will also keep them below ground.

During their active periods, they sprint from place to place, their tails held at a 45-degree angle. A typical pose when feeding or scanning the countryside is to sit upright on their haunches. Like many of their cousins, they use their paws for digging as well as for the manipulation of food. Although they are indifferent tree climbers, they are nimble among rocks and low shrubbery, and are strong swimmers.

Personality

Kenneth Gordon, associate professor of zoology at Oregon State College, wrote in his monograph on mantled ground squirrels:

If we live long enough and intimately enough with these animals each one in time comes to have an individuality of its own. This individuality shows itself in the way they ignore or enter into the experimental situations and devices and in their subsequent performance, in their social ranking, sometimes in certain mannerisms or actions. And it shows itself in more subtle ways that we are prone to describe in terms of human temperament. Some animals are phlegmatic, others excitable, and apt to cry wolf. Some are shy and retiring, others are bold. Some are easy going, some intense and dashing in their activities. Now and then, for some reason, one reminds us of somebody we know . . .

This species can be tame to the point of boldness, especially when coaxed with food. Dr. Gordon noted how quickly they lose their shyness, and observed: "Give them an oat and they will take the camp".

Habitat

Golden-mantled ground squirrels live in the highlands of southern Alberta and British Columbia. Some live above tree-line in the mountains; Ernest Thompson Seton wrote of them sharing the "rock castles" of their giant cousin, the yellow-bellied marmot. Many live in the foothills among jumbles of rock or the debris of talus. In the southern portion of their range, their favourite haunts are sunny glades among stands of fir, pine, or spruce. This type of terrain is ideal because it is open, yet there is enough ground cover for food, as well as plenty of stumps, fallen trees, and rocks for shelter.

The golden-mantled ground squirrel likes to site his den at the base of a tree or stump, in or beneath a fallen log, or among loose rocks at the foot of a slope. These locations offer him protection against predators, and a convenient observation platform. He differs from most of his relatives in that he removes all soil traces from both the main entrance, and the auxiliary entrances or bolt holes.

Most burrows are relatively simple, consisting of a shallow tunnel 2 to 5 m long, a small sleeping chamber, and possibly a store room. The sleeping chamber is lined with shredded vegetation, and not only accomodates the squirrel, but also host of mites, fleas, and ants.

When retiring for the night, this little rodent sometimes blocks the main entrance to his burrow with a plug of dried grass or leaves.

Feeding Habits

These ground squirrels are omnivores, preferring vegetation but also eating a wide variety of animal matter. This includes large insects, mice, fledgling birds, and eggs. Although most of their liquid requirements are filled by the moisture they obtain when eating plants, they will sometimes drink directly from streams and puddles.

Feeding is a serious business for both adult and juvenile golden-mantled ground squirrels; adults increase their body weight during the summer by approximately 60 per cent, while juveniles record a gain of more than 3000 per cent.

Most of their feeding takes place in the morning and, if necessary, they will travel several hundred metres to a bountiful food source such as a campground.

When they find themselves with more food than they need immediately, they provide for the future by filling their cheek pouches and carrying away as much as possible. Their cheek-pouch capacity is impressive; one squirrel managed to carry 360 grains of barley in a single load. A significant number of seeds that they bury are never recovered because of the demise of the owner, or his inability to remember the hiding place. Many of these seeds subsequently germinate.

Among the favourite items in their diet are the seeds of pine and fir, mushrooms, clover leaves, dandelion flowers, rosehips, strawberries, gooseberries, chokecherries, and grain.

Life Cycle

Male ground squirrels emerge from hibernation in mid-April. Depending upon the severity of the winter and the latitude, they may have to tunnel through more than 30 cm of snow to reach the sunlight. Instances of these squirrels tunnelling through more than 2 m of snow have also been recorded. Breeding commences when the females emerge a week or so later, and continues through May.

The litters, averaging 4 pups, are born in June after a gestation period of 28 days. At birth the pups are tiny, weighing only 6 g, but they grow very quickly. By the time they are a month old they have a full coat and weigh around 40 g; at three months they are two-thirds grown, and weigh approximately 140 g.

It is fortunate that juvenile ground squirrels grow rapidly because they are left to fend for themselves soon after they emerge from the natal den. This means they must find their own food, seek their own shelter, and cope with the agonistic behaviour of their elders, as well as the threat from predators.

Adult males are the first to hibernate, going underground at the beginning of September. Adult females (who have lost weight from bearing a litter) and their immature offspring remain active for several more weeks to put on as much fat as possible before the winter. However, even the heaviest juvenile is likely to weigh 25 g less than his parents, and he won't attain full growth or sexual maturity until the following spring.

Hibernation is Nature's way of protecting this species for the six-month period when snow covers their food supply, and sub-zero temperatures threaten their survival. Yet they frequently enter their winter quarters in the warmth of Indian summer, because their timetable is more strongly influenced by the declining amount of sunlight than by the temperature.

Although these squirrels store food in their hibernaculum, and they wake briefly every two weeks or so, relatively little is eaten during the winter. This cache is probably a reserve for the spring when much of the vegetation is still hidden under a layer of snow.

Golden-mantled ground squirrels sleep in a ball with their nose touching their toes, their ears tucked flat, and their tail covering their head and shoulders. Adult males are the first to go below ground in the autumn, and the first to emerge in the spring. Their winter-survival rate is better than that of juveniles, as they are full grown and more experienced. The adult males' behaviour often reminds one of the old adage "Early to bed, and early to rise . . ."

Natural Enemies
On land, predators of the golden-mantled ground squirrel are bears, cougars, coyotes, foxes, and weasels. Airborne predators such as Golden Eagles and buteo hawks also take their toll.

Golden-mantled ground squirrels are usually afflicted by fleas, ticks, and mites. These parasites are more of an ongoing nuisance than a serious threat to their lives.

Relations with Humans

Because their Canadian range is mostly removed from civilization, their activities have not conflicted with Man, and they have suffered little human interference.

Golden-mantled ground squirrels have an indirect economic value because they are a link in the food chain of valuable furbearing carnivores.

In the United States, these squirrels have been regarded as a detriment to reforestation because of their appetite for seeds and seedlings. Research indicates, however, that ground squirrels have practically no effect on a reforestation programme, and that many of the seeds they gather are inadvertently replanted.

Like many other mammals, these rodents occasionally carry ticks that transmit Rocky Mountain spotted fever, but this is the exception rather than the rule.

Where to Observe

Most of these little creatures are encountered by people hiking or camping in the foothills and mountains of their range. It is not always necessary to look for them—if you set up camp, there's a good chance they will come to you.

Eastern Chipmunk
Suisse
Tamias striatus

Common Names

This species is also known as the common chipmunk, big chipmunk, striped ground squirrel, chipmunk, and chippie. His French name, *le suisse*, is very old and was given to him by the Recollet missionary, Gabriel Sagard-Theodat, when he wrote *L'histoire du Canada* in 1636. Early English writers referred to the eastern chipmunk as a "mouse squirrel".

His scientific name, *Tamias striatus*, is a combination of Greek and Latin. *Tamias*, meaning "steward", is particularly appropriate because of his penchant for gathering and storing nuts, while *striatus*, meaning "striped", describes the pattern of his coat.

Description

The eastern chipmunk has the silhouette of a small tree-squirrel, except for his tail, which is only one-third as long as his body. Although melanistic and albino chipmunks are rare, it is normal for the colour shades in the coats of individual animals to vary. Most appear tawny-brown at a distance, and all have the same distinctive pattern of stripes: five dark-brown or black lines, separated by four buff lines. Because he is a chipmunk, rather than a ground squirrel, his stripes start near his whiskers and extend across his face. His russet-brown rump, and orange tail with grizzled guard hairs, contrast sharply with his creamy underparts.

This species usually moults twice each year. Throughout the Canadian range, the summer moult takes place in July and August and the autumn moult occurs during September and October. Mature chipmunks of both sexes attain an overall length of approximately 27 cm and weigh an average of 100 g.

Eastern Chipmunk

Canadian Range

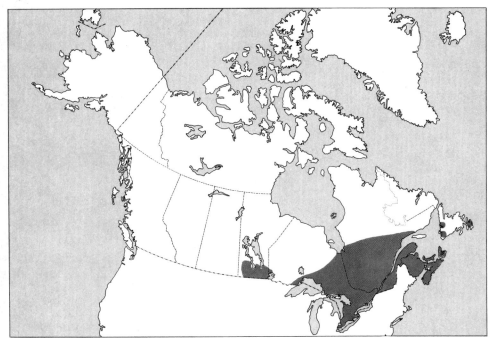

Range

The eastern chipmunk has a vast wedge-shaped range stretching from Newfoundland in the East to the Saskatchewan border in the West. He is found as far north as James Bay and Sept Isles, Quebec; and he is widely dispersed through the eastern United States, reaching as far south as Louisiana.

This is one of the two species introduced to Newfoundland in 1962. Thirty chipmunks were transplanted from the Tobeatic Game Sanctuary in Nova Scotia to Barachois Pond Provincial Park by the Newfoundland Wildlife Division. The experiment has proved a success; by 1973 the little band of settlers had not only multiplied, but dispersed over an area of approximately 800 km².

The population density of chipmunks varies widely throughout their range; an ideal habitat may contain as many as 25 adults to the hectare.

Behaviour

The eastern chipmunk lives alone or in family groups rather than in communities. However, in prime habitat, quite a few will often live in close proximity to each other. They are only active during daylight and retreat to the shelter of their dens during very warm or inclement weather.

Chipmunks are alert, bright, little creatures whose speed and mobility make them the "artful dodgers" of the forest. Most of their time is spent at ground level, but they climb well, and have been sighted feeding in beech and elm trees at heights of 20 m. They can also swim when necessary.

The home range for this species has been estimated as 0.20 ha for males and 0.10 ha for females. Home ranges frequently overlap when a number of these rodents occupy a restricted area. Agonistic behaviour is not a strong trait in chipmunks although it does occur, particularly during the mating seasons, and the losers may suffer serious wounds.

Chipmunks express their emotions with their tails and their voices. When they are agitated they make a chippering sound accompanied by spasmodic tail-twitches. When danger looms, they flee with their tails erect, emitting a series of chittering squeaks. When sizing up a potentially hostile neighbour, they may reveal their nervousness by sitting tensely and stamping their tiny feet in an alternating rhythm. During tranquil periods, they sometimes utter soft "cuck cuck" notes. These small mammals are seldom thought of as woodland vocalists, yet their "chip" sound is often heard on fine spring days. Ernest Thompson Seton wrote of this habit in *Lives of Game Animals* and printed a delightful photograph of a chipmunk serenading an audience of 12 English Sparrows.

In midsummer, chipmunks seem to disappear. Until recently, their disappearance was attributed to aestivation, a form of hibernation induced by the hot dry weather. Today most authorities agree that the seeming scarcity of chipmunks is attributable to the females raising litters, and to the heavy summer foliage, which masks the activity of the males. By autumn, when the leaves have thinned, chipmunks seem to magically reappear, the adults of both sexes as well as young of the year spending their waking hours gathering and storing food.

Personality

In 1923, A. Brooker Klugh, a professor on the staff of Queen's University, Kingston, published notes on the habits of the eastern chipmunk in the *Journal of Mammalogy* 4(1):32. In his paper Dr. Klugh told of three chipmunks he met near St. Andrews, New Brunswick: *One, subsequently called "Nipper", was the largest and greyest, "Fuzzy-tail" was distinguished by a somewhat scant-haired tail on which the hairs usually stood out almost at right angles and by a brighter coloration, and "Erythro" was so named on account of its very reddish coloration. . . .*

We began to give them peanuts, and at once the marked difference in their dispositions became apparent. Nipper was by far the boldest, and in a few days was taking food from our hands and climbing all over us. He seemed to have some difficulty in distinguishing between a peanut and the tip of one's finger, and the severe nips he administered because of this delusion earned him his name. If I held my hand 18 inches from the ground he would jump up onto it, and would jump up on my hand and take peanuts from between my teeth. Of the various chipmunks I have tamed Nipper was the only one which allowed himself to be stroked, as all the others have regarded the hand coming down to stroke them with suspicion and have jumped the second it touched them. Fuzzy-tail soon became tame and ran all over us, but was much more easily frightened than Nipper, and was also far gentler. Erythro, though it would sometimes come and feed from the hand, was always "jumpy" and very uncertain, being comparatively tame one day and quite timid the next.

Habitat

Eastern chipmunks live in areas where the ground is dry (which permits them to dig their burrows easily), and where there is sufficient low shrubbery to provide food and shelter; this combination is often found at the edge of mature forests. They are particularly fond of siting their burrows in brush heaps, stone walls, log fences, hedgerows, and log piles. When close to civilization, they frequently occupy abandoned buildings or structures such as a garage or barn, which have little human traffic.

Many locations that seemingly offer a suitable habitat are barren, while others host up to 25 chipmunks to the hectare. Normally an individual animal's home range is less than 0.50 ha but a distant food supply, or the mating urge, may cause it to travel several kilometres.

The burrow entrance is usually free of soil, and the funnel-shaped entrance hole, 5 to 10 cm in diameter, descends sharply for the first 15 to 20 cm. Then the tunnel narrows and the descent becomes more gradual to a depth of around 65 cm. At this level, the passage may continue parallel to the surface for up to 3 m before it terminates in an oval-shaped sleeping chamber. The sleeping chamber is lined with leaves, which the chipmunk has chewed into small pieces, and is approximately 32 cm in diameter.

Frequently, the same chipmunk will occupy the same burrow for a number of years, digging new tunnels each summer and sealing up old passages. In time, his burrow develops into a complicated maze consisting of several active entrances as well as the disused (plugged) ones.

The eastern chipmunk is an ingenious excavator, who employs a "work hole" to dispose of the subsoil that he displaces in his digging. When he has finished pushing the earth out of the tunnel with his nose, and the work is complete, he seals the work hole, with its obvious pile of debris, and uses a different entrance hole.

Feeding Habits

Most of the eastern chipmunk's food intake consists of vegetation, although at certain times he will happily consume animal matter such as June bugs, worms, grasshoppers, frogs, and occasionally, bird eggs. Like other small rodents, he obtains some of his liquid requirement from the stalks and leaves of plants, but he also drinks freely (sucking up the water like a horse, rather than lapping it like a dog), and he will eat snow.

In the spring, the chipmunks depend upon seeds hidden the previous year as well as the corms of various plants, and the samaras of maples and elms. During the summer, they have a wide choice of fruits and seeds, including strawberries, chokecherries, raspberries, blueberries, wild geraniums, dog-toothed violets and wintergreen. In the autumn, they concentrate on nuts, particularly those of the beech, hazel, and hickory trees, and acorns.

Chipmunks are noted for their habit of storing nonperishable seeds and nuts. As the summer wanes, they become totally preoccupied with this task so that by the time winter comes, they have frequently cached far more than they can eat. When gathering food, they hold the morsel in their front paws and separate the seeds from the fruit, or husk the kernel, with their teeth and tongue, deftly shifting the seeds or kernel back into their cheek pouches and spitting out the pulp. When their cheek pouches are full, they look as though they have a severe case of mumps. This is not surprising considering the type of loads they carry; one observer watched a chipmunk stuff 6 chestnuts into his cheeks (3 to each side), while Dr. Brooker Klugh counted 31 kernels of corn in the pouches of another.

Life Cycle

The spring breeding cycle for the eastern chipmunk is influenced by latitude and weather. Throughout most of Canada, these animals mate in the last weeks of March, and the young are born in late April or early May, after a gestation period of 31 days. The average litter consists of 4 to 5 pups, who are born blind and hairless, weighing around 3 g.

Within 3 weeks the babies have grown a silky coat, resembling their parents except for their tails, which are stubby and sparsely furred, like a rat's. Their eyes open in their fourth week and they become increasingly active in the nest. They emerge from the natal den 5 or 6 weeks after birth; by this time their tails have filled out, their coats are dense and they weigh around 50 g. A month or so later the young disperse and dig their own simple dens. While most juveniles don't mature sexually until the following year, it occasionally happens that a female will produce a litter the summer of her birth—at the age of three months.

It is normal for mature females to have a second oestrous cycle in mid-summer, around the beginning of July. Some of these females bear a second litter in August. Both adults and juveniles enter hibernation at the end of October or the beginning of November, which gives the young of second litters only a minimum time to prepare for winter. This is one of the reasons that more than half the young of the year die during their first winter.

During the last weeks of summer and in the early autumn, this chipmunk works feverishly to gather as many nuts and seeds as possible; many of these are stored under his bed of leaves in the sleeping chamber. When he retires, he blocks the entrance to his burrow with a plug of earth and vegetation, and then curls up in a ball, sitting on his tail, or lying on his side like a cat.

The eastern chipmunk wakes frequently through the winter; this is essential to his survival, for he is ill-equipped to withstand a long cold siege without food as he doesn't have a heavy layer of fat like some of the other Sciuridae.

The duration and extent of this chipmunk's hibernation vary across Canada with the latitude and severity of the weather. In southern Ontario, chipmunks are frequently seen during the coldest months; in the James Bay region they are inactive from October to April.

Most authorities estimate this chipmunk's life span in the wild to be 3 to 4 years, although captive animals have lived to be twice that age.

Natural Enemies

This diminutive rodent must be vigilant at all times, for he is sought by a host of predators. He is vulnerable to airborne attack by any of the hawks; on land, his most dangerous enemies are the weasel, ermine, and fox. Many chipmunks living close to civilization are caught by domestic cats.

Although the eastern chipmunk is fastidious about his personal cleanliness, and takes care not to foul his nest, he is often afflicted with mites and fleas that cause him discomfort. A more-serious parasite, the larva of the botfly (*Cuterebra emasculator*), becomes embedded in his groin, and eventually creates a large running sore.

Relations with Humans

The advance of civilization has had conflicting influences on the eastern chipmunk. In clearing the land, we have improved the habitat for this species and reduced the number of his predators. However, the automobile and the domestic cat have taken a fearsome toll of chipmunks over the years, and there is no reason to believe that these hazards will diminish in the future.

The eastern chipmunk is sometimes a nuisance to gardeners because he loves corn and flower bulbs. Fortunately, he is rarely present in sufficient numbers to cause serious damage, and he atones for his misdemeanours—to some extent—by eating grubs and insects.

He has no economic value, but the sight of this little fellow darting through the foliage provides many people with a great deal of pleasure.

Where to Observe

Eastern chipmunks live in, or near, most of the cities and towns in eastern Canada, and are one of the easiest mammals to approach. When I was a boy at the Y.M.C.A. camp at Golden Lake, Ontario, we used a trail of cherry pits or watermelon seeds to lure chipmunks into the cabins.

These saucy little animals make excellent subjects for outdoor photography.

Least Chipmunk
Tamia mineur
Eutamias* minimus

Common Names

Because of his diminutive size, this species is often called the little chipmunk, the little northern chipmunk, or, in French Canada, *le petit suisse* (the little Swiss). He is also known as the western chipmunk, and carries the same nicknames as his cousins, chippy and stripey.

His scientific name, *Eutamias minimus*, is a mixture of Greek and Latin, refering to his habit of hoarding seeds and his comparative size. *Eutamias* means "a good steward", while *minimus* means "least".

Description

This daintily made little animal is the smallest of our chipmunks, and has been described by the Canadian naturalist, J. Dewey Soper, as a "charming, sprightly elf".

The tawny coat of the least chipmunk is marked by five black stripes, which contrast sharply with four buff stripes. The sides of his head have three dark lines separated by two light lines. His underparts are white, and his long tail appears beige.

These chipmunks moult twice each year, donning their bright summer coat in July, and their more-subdued winter coat in late September or early October. Both sexes weigh approximately 50 g when full grown, but females who attain an overall length of 23 cm, are fractionally larger than the males who average 22 cm overall. This species can easily be confused with the yellow-pine and red-tailed chipmunks; when making an identification, it is important to check both range and habitat.

Least Chipmunk

*Some taxonomists have changed the genus name from *Eutamias* to *Tamias*

Canadian Range

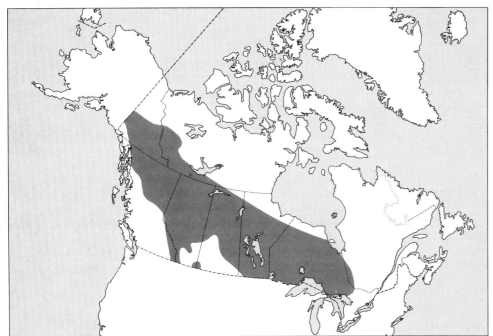

Range

The least chipmunk has a gigantic range, unlike his cousins the yellow-pine and red-tailed chipmunks, who are confined to southern British Columbia and southwestern Alberta. The range of the least chipmunk sweeps from the Northwest Territories through British Columbia, across the Prairie Provinces and a large part of Ontario, to the western edge of Quebec—a distance of 4200 km. Throughout this belt, there are many areas where the species is absent, but in suitable terrain there may be as many as 15 chipmunks to the hectare.

Behaviour

Although least chipmunks live alone, rather than in communities, they are quite gregarious. There is relatively little agonistic behaviour among families, and the only time adults quarrel is during the breeding season; even then, rival males are more inclined to chase than to fight.

They are strictly diurnal, normally emerging from their sleeping chambers shortly after dawn and returning before sunset. Most of their day is spent gathering food, a task they approach with considerable enthusiasm. Although they are ground dwellers, they are also expert climbers, and can flit through the branches with the dexterity of a tree squirrel. When moving from one place to another, they may creep along with their tails held horizontally; more often they scurry at high speed, with their tails held at a 45- to 90-degree angle. At rest, they like to sit on a rock or log and soak up the sun. Rather surprisingly, these little animals do most of their foraging quite close to their dens; the average range is approximately 0.10 ha.

Despite the preoccupation with stocking their larders, least chipmunks are finely tuned to the sounds of the forest and quick to heed a warning cry from other species. They are also chatterboxes in their own right, and can be counted on to comment loudly on any occurrence, particularly an intruder's entrance into their territory. They have a variety of calls, which include rasping, chittering and chirping sounds. All their calls have an elusive quality, like the voice of a ventriloquist, and are hard to locate. The surest way to confirm their location is to watch for the flicking of their tail, which twitches in the same rhythm as the call.

They are noted for their personal cleanliness and seem to take pride in keeping their coats shiny and bright. Grooming is done with their hands and feet, which, in turn, are washed with their tongues. Because fleas and mites are a recurring problem, they resort to frequent dust baths. Parasites are dislodged with the particles of dust when the chipmunk shakes himself after his bath.

Personality

In *Lives of Game Animals*, Ernest Thompson Seton quotes his friend, Miller Christy, who visited an abandoned sawmill near Carberry, Manitoba:

I went on another day to the mill in order to try and catch some Chipmunks alive. This I found a very easy thing to do with a figure-4 box-trap. The animals seemed perfectly unsuspecting. Whilst I was setting one of these, a Chipmunk extracted my small store of bait from the paper in which it was wrapped, and consumed a considerable portion of it. As the little thief scampered off at my approach, with every appearance of laughing at me, he dropped the bread, and I secured it; but I had no sooner done this than on looking round, I found that another Chipmunk was sitting upright on the top of the trap I had just set, nibbling at my bait, which he held in his fore paws, and eyeing me sharply; but otherwise manifesting a coolness and deliberateness of procedure that completely staggered me.

Habitat

Because of his vast range, the least chipmunk lives in a variety of terrain. Forest edges and the second growth that follows a fire or lumbering are his favourite haunts, owing to his partiality for both sunlight and a protective ground-cover. However, he is also found in brushy spots on the alpine tundra and the sagebrush plains, as well as in clearings in dense coniferous forests. In the areas where his range overlaps that of the yellow-pine chipmunk, the least chipmunk is usually found in the rocky fringe at or above timberline.

Least chipmunks usually occupy different homes in summer and winter. Their summer residence can be a tunnel at the base of a stump, a crevice among loose stones, or a nest in a fallen log. During this season, they sometimes live in trees, in a shaggy round nest built of leaves and grass; or they claim "squatters' rights" in an abandoned woodpecker's hole. Their winter home is a subterranean burrow sited among trees, where fallen leaves provide additional insulation when the snow comes.

A typical burrow has a small concealed entrance, and a single tunnel, 1 m in length, leading to the sleeping chamber, which is approximately 16 cm in diameter, and is usually located about 30 cm below ground level.

When excavating the burrow, the chipmunk digs an auxiliary "work hole", which is used to store the displaced soil. When the job is finished, the work hole is plugged with earth, and the chipmunk uses his "front door".

A Original hole filled in
B Main entrance
C Main passage
D Nest

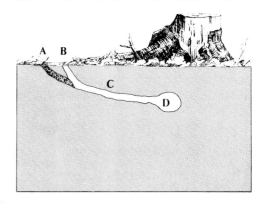

Feeding Habits

Least chipmunks are mainly herbivores, but they will occasionally consume a small amount of animal matter in the form of grasshoppers, beetles, and caterpillars. Possibly because of their small size, they rarely eat larger invertebrates, and definitely prefer seeds.

These rodents are industrious seed-gatherers, who can transport prodigious loads in their expandable cheek pouches. Various reports have attested to their tremendous cheek-pouch capacity—one chipmunk was carrying more than 100 cherry stones when he was caught, another had 3,700 blueberry seeds.

Some food is cached directly in their dens, but most is hidden nearby; large items such as acorns are buried singly, while small seeds like timothy are buried in clumps. They suffer a considerable loss because of pilferage by other rodents and their own forgetfulness. Some of the buried seeds subsequently grow into trees and plants.

These chipmunks will drink freely, but they normally get most of their water requirement from vegetation. When eating, they use their paws like hands and, despite their tiny size, they frequently manage with one paw. Although they are very fond of fruits and berries, they usually strip away the pulp and only eat the seeds. A neat little pile of fruit pulp on a log or stone is their telltale signature.

Among the staples in their diet are: seeds of many grasses and sedges, strawberries, rose hips, blueberries, raspberries, cherry pits, acorns, and hazelnuts. They don't eat poison-ivy berries.

Life Cycle

Because of their extensive range, it is difficult to state a common timetable throughout Canada for these chipmunks. However, in most parts of the country, the males emerge from hibernation, or become active, around the end of March and a week or so later they are joined by the females. Breeding takes place during April, a month marked by frequent chases and skirmishes among rival males.

The gestation period is between 28 and 30 days, with the young being born around the middle of May. An average litter consists of 5 tiny, pink-skinned pups, who are born blind and deaf, weighing 2.25 g. The infants stay with their mother for approximately 8 weeks.

If she has to move them during this period, she carries them, one at a time, by the skin of their belly—they make a compact bundle with their head and tail curled around her neck. Should she lose her litter before they are grown, she may breed again and have another family late in the summer.

Juvenile chipmunks, when they disperse at the age of two months, are almost the same size as adults, but they do not fully mature until the following spring.

Time of hibernation varies with the latitude; however, regardless of the area, adult males precede females and juveniles into retirement. Least chipmunks, like other small mammals, are subject to fluctuations of abundance and decline. Under ideal conditions, they can live at least 6 years in the wild.

Least chipmunks become dormant throughout most of their range by the beginning of November. Their withdrawal may last up to 6 months, or it may be sporadic; the schedule depends upon latitude and weather; on the alpine tundra it will last all winter, in the temperate south it may only last for a few days at a time.

During the late summer, they cache a substantial amount of seeds in their burrows; as many as 478 acorns, or 2,734 cherry pits have been found. They also line their sleeping chambers with grasses, shredded leaves, and the down from catkins. Because they don't build a thick layer of fat like other hibernators, the food store is vital for their survival, and is located conveniently beneath their bed.

Prior to hibernation, they plug the tunnel leading to the sleeping chamber with earth and vegetation. Then they curl up on their haunches, with their tail thrown over their head, and go to sleep. Most emerge or become fully active by the end of March.

Natural Enemies

The least chipmunk has many enemies. Hawks make frequent attacks and owls sometimes snatch the unwary. Fortunately, owls pose a minor threat since most are nocturnal hunters and chipmunks are only active during the day.

On land, this rodent is vunerable to snakes and to every carnivore from the slender weasel to the powerful grizzly bear.

Relations with Humans

The least chipmunk usually lives in areas remote from civilization. The few that dwell near settlements are rarely concentrated to the extent that their seed-eating creates a problem. For these reasons, they have not been subjected to systematic extermination programmes.

Undoubtedly, he is guilty of eating the seeds of worthwhile plants and trees. But he is also responsible for accidentally planting a great many seeds that would never have germinated, and he accounts for a host of harmful insects during the course of a summer.

The least chipmunk's greatest value cannot be measured, for it is impossible to put a price on the pleasure he gives to people as he scampers about his daily business.

Where to Observe

This is one of the easiest animals to see because of the variety of terrain he favours and the vast extent of his range.

Keep your ears and eyes open; as soon as you hear his chirp, watch for the flick of his tail. If you are patient, and remain still, he may literally eat out of your hand.

Yellow-pine Chipmunk
Tamia amène
Eutamias* amoenus

Common Names

The yellow-pine chipmunk is sometimes called a northwestern chipmunk
because of his range; or a buff-bellied
chipmunk, because of the distinctive
colour of his underparts. Like other chipmunks, he is also nicknamed chippy or
stripey.

His scientific name, *Eutamias
amoenus*, is most appropriate. *Eutamias*
is a combination of Greek and Latin
meaning "a good steward", while
amoenus is Latin for "delightful".

Description

The yellow-pine chipmunk has the
same pattern of stripes as his two western
cousins, the least chipmunk and the red-
tailed chipmunk. Three dark stripes cross
his cheeks, the middle one running
through the eye; these darker stripes are
separated by two pale stripes. Five dark
stripes separated by four pale stripes run
along his back; the median one, running
from the forehead to the base of the
spine, is the longest. The major difference is that the yellow-pine chipmunk is
slightly larger than the least chipmunk,
and a trifle smaller than the red-tailed
chipmunk. In addition, the yellow-pine is
midway between the other two in coloration, having a more richly coloured coat
than the least chipmunk and a slightly
paler coat than the red-tailed chipmunk.
Because these three chipmunks are easily
confused, it is important to consider the
range and habitat when making an identification.

The dark dorsal and lateral lines on
the yellow-pine chipmunk are chocolate-
brown, and the light lines are beige. His
shoulders and flanks have an orange
coat, while his rump is brownish grey.
His underparts—a useful field mark—are
normally buff, but may be so pale as to
appear white. The backs of his ears are
black. His relatively long tail is a rusty
hue above and tawny-coloured on the
underside.

This species moults twice each year,
and there is often a visible line between
the old and new fur. Males change their
pelage several weeks earlier than females,
donning their bright summer coat in June
and July, and their more-subdued winter
coat in September and October.

Adults of both sexes grow to an
overall length of approximately 23 cm,
and weigh an average of 55 g by late
summer.

Yellow-pine Chipmunk

*Some taxonomists have changed the genus name
from Eutamias to Tamias*

Canadian Range

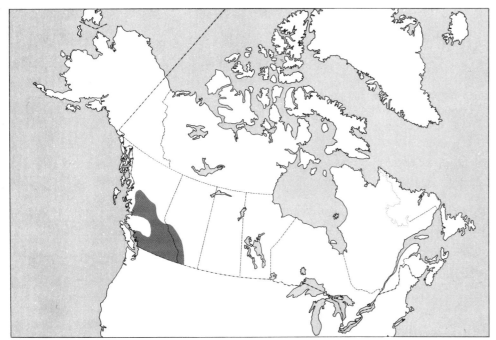

Range

In Canada, the yellow-pine chipmunk is found in the mountains of southern British Columbia and southwestern Alberta, at elevations from 800 m to around 2000 m. His continental range extends from California to the Skeena River in British Columbia. In the state of Washington, he has been observed at altitudes exceeding 4500 m.

Because much of the mountainous terrain within his range is unsuitable habitat, population densities vary from area to area. Some regions are unpopulated, while others with pockets of favourable habitat may support as many as 6 chipmunks to the hectare.

Behaviour

The yellow-pine chipmunk is a solitary little creature who minds his own business. Although he is territorial to some extent, and the territories often overlap, aggressive behaviour is rarely shown. The only exception is when the young are nursed. In this instance, a lactating female will usually chase away intruders who come within 50 m of her den. After the young are weaned, she too adopts an attitude of *laisser-faire*. When two chipmunks meet, they identify each other by sniffing the other's face and neck; this ritual lasts about five or six seconds.

Yellow-pine chipmunks are diurnal, with the main peaks of activity taking place in the early morning and late afternoon. They don't mind cloudy weather or a light drizzle, but heavy rain or high winds tend to restrict their movements. By half an hour after sunset, all have retired to their dens for the night. Usually they sleep curled up in a ball, with their paws over their face.

H.E. Broadbooks, an American student of yellow-pine chipmunks, has identified at least ten different calls. The most common are the high-pitched chirp of alarm and the scolding rattle used to chase away an intruder. In a comprehensive article for the Museum of Zoology, University of Michigan, Dr. Broadbooks wrote:

Another call frequently used was a low, mellow note that sounded like a robin, and which I described as pert (*also as* pwert, pyert, *or* whirt). *Chipmunks were able to make this sound with full cheek pouches. Individuals, after release and when running away, gave this call. It was occasionally uttered after a hawk or jay has passed over. One chipmunk expressed his excitement with this call when he found a melon rind. His chirps were recorded as* pert pert pert-pert pert *and as* kwst pert kwst. *With each utterance his tail waved forward or backward. There was usually one note per second, but occasionally two in rapid succession. . . .*

These little chipmunks are nimble climbers, whose movements consist of jerky spurts punctuated by frequent twitches of their tails. Much of their time is spent feeding or gathering food for storage. When feeding, they work busily but may only cover a distance of 200 m in an hour. One of the reasons for their slow progress is the need to pause every few moments and check for danger; they frequently use boulders and low shrubbery as observation posts.

They are clean little animals and spend part of each day grooming their fur with their paws, and taking dust baths. A dust bath is the "full treatment" because it not only helps to get rid of fleas and other parasites, but it also prevents their fur from getting too oily.

Personality

Don Meredith, a writer and biologist from Alberta, who has studied the yellow-pine chipmunk extensively, wrote me about one of these chipmunks that he kept as a house pet. The little creature's food was kept in a container at the top of a tall bookcase. One day the chipmunk figured out where his food was and set about to get it:

Through the course of the evening the animal made forays from one shelf to the next in search of the seeds he knew were there. The trail was tricky. It involved climbing up on books and bending backwards out in space to get to the next shelf. Often an attempt ended in a fall to the floor. There he would pick himself up and try again. As the evening wore on the chipmunk got higher and higher, but each attempt ended with him pitching head over heels to the carpet.

Finally the conversation in the room turned to the striped elf who was about to make his last ascent. A cheer arose when he swung himself up and reached the container. He couldn't open it, so I removed the top of the tin and let him fill his pouches. He then scampered down the bookshelf and deposited his booty in his nest.

Moments later he was on his way back up the book case. This time, he was able to open the container himself. On his third trip he again entered the tin to fill his pouches, but he suddenly changed his mind, jumped out of the container, and pushed it off the shelf onto the floor. Then he flew down the bookcase and commenced to transfer the mess of sunflower seeds and oats into his nest. At this point I decided enough was enough, and confiscated the container, after replacing most of the spilled contents.

The chipmunk was in a rage at this turn of events, and let me know precisely how he felt about the injustice with a series of staccato chips and much chattering of teeth. I admired his talent and determination as a problem solver, but didn't feel too badly, because his nest was already overflowing with food he had gathered during the past weeks.

Habitat

The yellow-pine chipmunk is found in grassy areas in valleys and also in clearings among stands of coniferous and deciduous trees. He prefers areas with ground cover consisting of low shrubs and bushes or tall plants such as lupine, and he is often spotted near scattered rocks or windfalls. In the mountainous areas of Canada, this chipmunk normally occupies the belt between 800 m and tree-line. As a general rule, when the ranges of the yellow-pine and the least chipmunk overlap, the least chipmunk will occupy the rocky, more alpine, areas close to or above tree-line.

The home range of the yellow-pine chipmunk is difficult to pinpoint because of the variety of terrain, and because the total area covered by males is greater than that covered by females. A study done in the Alberta Rockies by Dr. David Sheppard of the University of Saskatchewan revealed that males had a range of approximately 1.25 ha, while females had a range of approximately .50 ha.

The yellow-pine chipmunk occupies both underground dens and arboreal nests. Hibernation and the bearing of young usually take place below ground, while tree nests are often used as a summer residence by adults, and as a second-stage home for young families.

Favourite sites for underground dens include the base of stumps; beneath windfalls; and in the crevices of rocks. Many burrows are dug in loose soil and may be recognized by the neat entrance hole, which averages 5 cm in diameter. From the entrance, the tunnel descends to a circular chamber, approximately 13 cm wide, which is lined with grass. Frequently, a short blind alley intersects the tunnel between the entrance hole and the chamber. When this type of den is used as a hibernaculum, the floor of the sleeping chamber is stocked with seeds, and the bed may be lined with thistle-down, fur, or feathers, as well as shredded vegetation.

Tree nests are made of grass, and are usually located in low trees, such as willows, at a height of around 2 to 3 m. This type of home has an outer diameter of approximately 35 cm, which gives it the appearance of a large roofed-over bird's nest. The interior of a tree nest is roomier than an underground burrow, and is lined in the same way. Frequently, a yellow-pine chipmunk will occupy a disused woodpecker's hole, or build a nest in a tall stump.

Feeding Habits

The yellow-pine chipmunk deserves his name "good steward", for he will climb anything from a thistle stalk to a pine tree 30 m high to collect food. The thistle is a good example of his talent; not only can he climb the prickly plant with impunity, but he can manipulate the head of the flower with his paws so that he extracts the seeds without injury.

Most of his diet consists of seeds and flowers. His favourite seeds are those of the larch, yellow-pine, and douglas-fir trees, although he also enjoys the seeds of sedges, knotweed, and grasses, especially timothy. The balance is made up of fruits, nuts, corms, fungi, and animal matter. The most striking features about his menu are the small size of the individual items and the prodigious work required to collect enough to make a meal. Despite the need to deal with numerous tiny particles, he seems to enjoy his food immensely. It is a common sight to see one of these little fellows sitting on his haunches, with his tail waving from side to side, as he rotates a morsel with his paws and eats it with obvious relish. As the summer progresses, food is cached for the winter. When he harvests seeds, the chipmunk stuffs his cheek pouches and then returns to his den or cache. Studies tell of one yellow-pine chipmunk who had 264 buck-brush seeds in his cheeks while another was carrying 1,650 wild-cranberry seeds. These numbers pale when an inventory of their winter cache is taken; 14,000 seeds is not unusual and one hibernating den contained 68,000 items!

Life Cycle

In Canada, yellow-pine chipmunks emerge from hibernation during March and April. Regardless of the date, which is dependent upon the altitude and the severity of the winter, there is still a lot of snow in the high country. Mating takes place soon after emergence, and the young are born in late April or May, following a gestation period of approximately 28 days. The average litter consists of 6 pups, each weighing approximately 2 g. At birth, the hairless infants are deaf and blind, but able to make little squeaking sounds. By the time the pups are 10 days old, faint stripes are visible in their downy coats. At about 3 weeks, they begin to climb awkwardly about the den; 5 weeks after their birth their eyes open and it is at this time that their mother often transfers her family to a tree nest. One reason for moving above ground is to get away from the parasites and excrement in the natal den. Tree nests are also roomier than underground burrows, provide greater safety from land predators, and make an excellent playground where the young can exercise. By August, the juveniles are well grown, and many disperse. Initially, this is a time of high mortality, for the juveniles are curious and naïve, which makes them an easy prey for predators. The young that survive this test hibernate at the same time as the adults, usually during September and October.

Yellow-pine chipmunks hibernate for approximately five months of the year. Prior to hibernation, they prepare an underground den by lining it with grasses and shredded vegetation, and lay in a considerable store of seeds. During hibernation, they wake periodically to eat and to eliminate body wastes.

Tests have shown that up to 97 per cent of the yellow-pine chipmunks entering hibernation in the autumn survive the winter. Thus, for this species, the long period of torpor is undoubtedly the safest time in their lives.

Despite the harsh environment, and a host of predators, the yellow-pine chipmunk may live as long as 5 years in the wild.

Natural Enemies

The long-tailed weasel is the most dangerous land predator, because it has the speed and agility to follow chipmunks in the trees, and can sometimes squeeze its way into an underground den. The pine marten can also catch a chipmunk above ground. Other land enemies are the bobcat, the coyote, and the rattlesnake. The yellow-pine chipmunk is vulnerable to attack from the air by hawks and the Pygmy Owl, who hunts during daylight.

This chipmunk is infested by ticks, fleas, mites, lice, and the botfly, whose larvae burrow beneath his skin. He is also the victim of parasitic worms, especially tapeworms, which can eventually kill their host.

Relations with Humans

Yellow-pine chipmunks live at high altitudes in terrain that is usually remote from civilization; thus Man has had little effect on the species.

He eats a number of insects that are harmful to trees, and also inadvertently contributes to reforestation when seeds he has cached germinate. However, his main value cannot be measured, for it is impossible to put a price on the pleasure he gives wilderness travellers.

Where to Observe

The yellow-pine chipmunk is a common visitor to campgrounds and picnic sites throughout his range. He is normally somewhat timid, but the offer of a nut or sunflower seed will quickly make him lose his shyness.

Townsend's Chipmunk
Tamia de Townsend
Eutamias* townsendii

Common Names

This species is sometimes called the western chipmunk. He also shares with other members of the *Eutamias* genus a host of affectionate nicknames including chip, chippy, striper, and stripey.

His scientific name, *Eutamias townsendii*, is a mixture of two classical languages. *Eutamias* is a combination of Greek and Latin meaning "a good steward"—a title that is well deserved because of his penchant for caching seeds. *Townsendii* is the Latinized surname of his discoverer, John Townsend, who was best known as an ornithologist, but who also identified a number of mammals, including this chipmunk, while accompanying Thomas Nuttall's expedition to Oregon in 1834.

Description

Although he only weighs 85 g, and is delicately built, the Townsend's chipmunk is the largest of the chipmunks in western Canada.

A chipmunk is easily distinguished from a ground squirrel because the lines on the chipmunk's coat extend across his face. The Townsend's chipmunk has the same pattern of stripes as his cousins—a broad dark band running from nose to tail, with two thin stripes on each side, which start above and below his eye. His blackish lines are separated by brownish lines, but there is little contrast because his pelt is very dark and he looks as though he has just had a bath in a cup of coffee. His underparts are tan, and his bushy tail, which is almost as long as his body, is a tawny grey-brown.

This species moults twice each year. Males moult in July and October, which is earlier than the females, who complete their summer moult in August, and don their winter coats in November. Both sexes attain a similar adult weight of 85 g, but females are a little larger, averaging 27 cm overall length, as against 25 cm for males.

Townsend's Chipmunk

Canadian Range

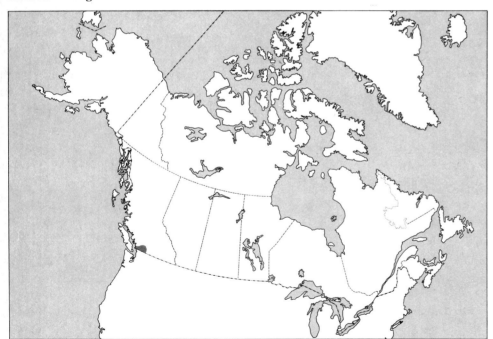

Range

The southwestern corner of British Columbia, including Garibaldi Provincial Park, Manning Provincial Park, and the southern portion of Vancouver Island, is the northern extremity of this chipmunk's continental range. Within this area, Townsend's chipmunks are found in suitable habitat from sea level to altitudes of more than 2000 m. Population density is relatively sparse, rarely exceeding five adults to the hectare.

Behaviour

Townsend's chipmunks are diurnal, with their most active periods being early and late in the day. Like their kin, they love the warmth of the sun, but too much heat causes them discomfort and frequently drives them to the shade of their den. An American naturalist once saw a chipmunk eating a choice morsel of food on a sun-drenched ledge. The stone was obviously too hot for comfort, so the little creature shifted his weight to his heels, and held the bare soles of his feet clear of the rock. During cold or wet weather, they spend most of the day in their burrow and restrict their foraging to a minimum.

It is rare to see a chipmunk moving at a walk. Normally, they scamper from place to place with their tail held at either a forty-five degree angle or straight up. When they reach their destination they immediately freeze in position, or sit alertly on their haunches; there is nothing casual about their movements. Although they are ground dwellers, they are expert climbers and can jump from branch to branch with ease. In some areas, they spend a great percentage of their time above ground level, at heights of more than 20 m, and they not only cache their food in trees, but also use them as nesting sites.

This chipmunk is considered to be relatively silent, but he has a repertoire of calls, most of which are chittering sounds uttered in varying cadences. Whatever call he chooses, it is sure to be accompanied by the brisk metronome beat of his tail. When danger threatens, he usually doesn't make a sound until he reaches a safe spot; then he puts his whole body into making a loud, emphatic call. Although these chipmunks live in small family groups, or alone, the prospect of food will cause a crowd of them to materialize as if by magic. Yet, even in the midst of a bonanza such as a well-stocked campsite, they often defer the pleasure of eating until they have carried away numerous loads of food in their cheek pouches for later consumption. Because they cache seeds in so many different places, some are invariably overlooked. These forgotten seeds grow into trees, confirming the role of the Townsend's chipmunk's as an accidental contributor to reforestation.

Personality

Miller Christy, a friend of Ernest Thompson Seton, had this to say in *Lives of Game Animals:*

Without exception, the chipmunk is in its form and movements the very prettiest little animal I ever set eyes on. . . . In it the fear of man seems to be entirely absent; it seems to run away merely for fun; *but for all that, you would almost as easily catch a flash of lightning! It is incessantly upon the move, climbing about and over everything as if exploring, and always carrying its long tail bolt upright in such a ridiculous manner that it becomes by far the most conspicuous part of the whole animal. You may see one of these tails, with a Chipmunk attached to it, dodging round a piece of wood and eyeing you keenly, without the slightest appearance of fear, as if roguishly trying to tempt you to catch it. But try! In a moment, with a shrill, derisive, bird-like whistle, the tail is gone—you hardly know where; till you see it again a moment later, going through exactly the same antics along with several other tails.*

Habitat

The favourite haunt of the Townsend's chipmunk is the dense, fern-shaded, coastal forest. However he is also found along log-strewn beaches; at sea level; and in subalpine forest cuttings with ample ground-cover, at altitudes as high as 2000 m.

In British Columbia, suitable terrain will host approximately five chipmunks to the hectare, each with a home range encompassing slightly less than 1 ha.

The entrance to the den of a Townsend's chipmunk is an inconspicuous hole at the base of a tree or stump, or a crevice among a jumble of rocks. Typically, a single tunnel descends for about 30 cm, before levelling off and running for another metre, where it terminates in a small sleeping chamber. This coconut-sized room contains a snug nest of shredded vegetation, and may have a hoard of seeds beneath the bed.

However, he may also site his den in a hollow log, and recent research in California has revealed that some members of this species nest in trees. Dr. L.R. Brand, of Loma Linda University, discovered five different families of Townsend's chipmunks living in fir trees at heights of up to 27 m above ground. It is reasonable to assume that tree nesting also occurs in this chipmunk's Canadian range.

Feeding Habits

Townsend's chipmunks are classed as omnivores since their diet includes a substantial amount of animal matter. These little rodents are industrious food-gatherers who may travel more than a kilometre to a lush source of supply. They are also noted for the carrying capacity of their expandable cheek-pouches, which can hold more than 100 oats or 1,000 cinnamon seeds at a time. Many of the seeds they garner are buried or hidden away for the future—hence their scientific name, *Eutamias*, "the good steward".

They are dextrous with their paws, which they use not only to eat with, but also to husk and strip edibles. When harvesting bushes, they often perform acrobatic feats such as hanging upside down to reach a distant branch. Tall stalks or other plants present little difficulty; they merely grasp the herbage near the ground, and pull it down paw over paw. Once they have obtained the morsel, they sit on their haunches and chew it with the speed of a sewing machine.

In Canada, staples of their menu are: roots; bulbs; grasses; conifer seeds; dandelion heads, particularly those that have just finished blooming; hazelnuts; berries; and large insects. They also eat birds' eggs, as well as fledglings, and are not above cannibalism.

Life Cycle

In British Columbia, male Townsend's chipmunks become fully active in late April or early May. They are joined a week or 10 days later by the females, and mating takes place during May. The young are born in June after a gestation period of approximately 30 days. Litters range in size from 2 to 7 infants with the average being 5.

At birth, the blind and hairless babies weigh less than 4 g. When they are ready to be weaned at approximately 5 weeks, they have a dense coat, and have increased their weight tenfold. A few weeks later, they disperse and seek their own homes; by the end of August they are fully grown.

Both adults and juveniles hibernate late in the autumn. Old males become inactive at the end of September, while females and juveniles seek their nests at the end of October. Young of the year will be sexually mature the following spring.

Townsend's chipmunks are intermittent hibernators; the amount of time they spend curled up in their den is governed by the climate and altitude. In the southern or coastal part of their range, many remain active all winter, while those in the northern or alpine regions are dormant for the coldest months.

Unlike ground squirrels, these chipmunks do not build up a heavy layer of fat in preparation for winter. Although they store seeds and nonperishable vegetation in their den, they enter hibernation with few reserves to draw upon. During the winter, they must wake frequently to eat from their cache and to eliminate body wastes. In some temperate areas, these chipmunks continue to forage as long as food is available. Should heavy snow blanket the ground, Nature induces a temporary state of anorexia and lassitude, which permits them to hibernate through the unseasonable weather without requiring much food.

In British Columbia, animals living near the coast are active most of the winter, while those in the high country spend the coldest months (December to March) asleep in their dens.

This species is relatively long-lived; individual animals have survived at least 7 years in the wild.

Natural Enemies

These little rodents fill an important ecological role by converting vegetable matter into animal food for carnivores. Chipmunks eat vegetation, and in turn are eaten by carnivores.

Skyborne buteo hawks and Golden Eagles are always on the lookout for a chipmunk who has strayed from the safety of cover. On land, their most dangerous enemy is the weasel, because weasels can not only catch them in the trees, but are slim enough to follow them into their dens. Other land predators are: badgers, foxes, marten, lynx, skunks, coyotes, wolverines, fishers, and raccoons.

Relations with Humans

Townsend's chipmunks are not sufficiently prevalent in any area of British Columbia to be a pest. In fact, most live in densely forested areas remote from civilization. Thus they have not attracted the attention (or wrath) of humans, and have been left alone.

Being seed eaters, these chipmunks can interfere with reforestation, although this damage is modified because they inadvertently "plant" some of the seeds they steal.

This species has no direct economic value, but most people derive real pleasure from simply seeing him frolic in the woods.

Where to Observe

Townsend's chipmunk is quite shy and tends to remain hidden in the undergrowth. If you are walking in his territory he will probably reveal his position by scolding you with a staccato series of chirps.

Red-tailed Chipmunk
Tamia à queue rousse
Eutamias * *ruficaudus*

Common Names

This species is also known as the rufous-tailed chipmunk; it is a fitting name, because "rufous" precisely describes the red-brown colour of the underside of his tail.

His formidable scientific name, *Eutamias ruficaudus*, also makes good sense. *Eutamias* is a combination of Greek and Latin meaning "a good steward", while *ruficaudus* is a compound Latin word made up of *rufus* "red" and *cauda* "tail".

Description

The red-tailed chipmunk is larger and more brightly coloured than the least and yellow-pine chipmunks, but he is easily confused with them when viewed from a distance because he has the same pattern of stripes. The dark stripe running from between his ears to his tail is black, as are the two upper ones on each side. These stripes are separated by pale-grey lines; the lower stripe on each side is brown, edged with white. The dark stripes on his face are also brown, and the light stripes are white. His shoulders and flanks are tawny, while his rump is olive-brown, and his underparts are pale buff or cream-coloured. A useful field-mark to note is his black-bordered tail, which is rich brown above, and brilliant rufous on the underside. Two additional factors to consider when making a positive identification are his range and habitat.

Like the other western chipmunks, this species undergoes two moults each year. His bright summer coat comes in during June and July, and is replaced by a less-colourful winter coat in September and October. The average overall length for adults is 23 cm, while the average weight for both sexes is approximately 60 g.

Red-tailed Chipmunk

Canadian Range

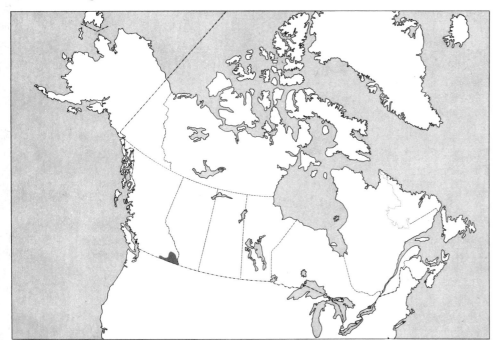

Range

The northern portion of the red-tailed chipmunk's range forks into Canada on either side of the Continental Divide, with the western prong extending to the Kootenay Valley in British Columbia, and the eastern prong reaching into Banff National Park in Alberta. Throughout his continental range, which includes parts of Washington, Idaho, and Montana, he is usually found at altitudes from 1300 to 2400 m.

Behaviour

The red-tailed chipmunk is a solitary creature who pays little attention to his own kind, except in the spring, which is the mating season. In British Columbia and Alberta, his distributional range overlaps that of his close relative, the yellow-pine chipmunk. Although both species have similar tastes and habits, they live in harmony because each occupies a slightly different niche in the environment. The red-tailed chipmunk is more arboreal and lives at and below timberline, while the yellow-pine chipmunk lives at lower elevations. When the least chipmunk is also present, he is compelled to eke out his existence in the sparsely vegetated fringes above timberline.

The red-tailed chipmunk is vulnerable to many predators. For this reason he pauses frequently to scan his surroundings and is constantly on the alert for danger. His alarm note is a single high-pitched *chirp*, accompanied by a twitch of his tail. Should the enemy approach more closely, this call will be repeated more loudly and more frequently. If he is forced to flee, he will be chattering like a machine gun by the time he reaches safety. Chipmunks also employ a staccato sound when scolding or chasing their own kind.

The chipmunks have keen eyesight and a well-developed sense of smell. Both senses help to protect them from danger, and are invaluable in locating food and differentiating between edible and inedible items. Laboratory tests have shown that they can detect buried food with their nose, and they can also locate food items solely on the strength of visual clues. Like the other chipmunks, they have a deep-seated instinct to hoard non-perishable foods, especially seeds. Even when their appetite has been sated, they continue to hoard—which is like going to the supermarket for next week's groceries immediately after a big meal. Hunger makes a difference in their hoarding pattern, however, for then they stow the food in their den rather than outside it.

The hoarding instinct is rarely admired in humans, but it is vital to the survival of chipmunks. When they enter hibernation, the red-tailed chipmunk and his cousins have little excess body fat—unlike the marmots. During the winter, chipmunks wake periodically to eat from their cache and to eliminate body wastes. If they didn't hoard systematically during the summer, their larder would soon be empty, and they would starve to death.

The red-tailed chipmunk is diurnal; sometimes his day starts before sunrise but he is invariably back in his nest by nightfall. A.W.F. Banfield, author of *The Mammals of Canada*, observed this species in Alberta and wrote:
They spent much of their time in the low branches of coniferous trees. They were also particularly lively and uttered quick chattering calls reminiscent of small-scale red squirrels.

Personality

Cy Hampson, a well-known naturalist from Edmonton, wrote me about his first encounter with red-tailed chipmunks. This took place on a sunny September day, in Waterton Lakes National Park, Alberta.

I had been hiking along a trail which wended its way through a thick stand of lodgepole pine and then opened into a boulder-strewn clearing, carpeted with dense undergrowth. On reaching the clearing, I was immediately aware of the bird-like notes of chipmunks scurrying for cover. I leaned against a shoulder-high boulder and waited quietly.

During the next few minutes the rufous-tails reappeared; there must have been a dozen of them. The first sign of their presence was the sudden swaying of individual rose bushes, while the plants around them remained motionless. In a moment or two, brightly furred chipmunks could be seen clinging to the tops of thorny twigs, deftly nipping the stems of rose hips, which they allowed to fall to the ground. Then they would dash down the stems, retrieve their prizes, and take them to the summit of nearby boulders. Here, they perched on their haunches and quickly rolled the rose hips in their fore-paws, while sharp incisors neatly removed the pulp, exposing the amber seeds. They worked industriously, stuffing their cheek pouches until they could hold no more. Then up at a sharp angle went their long slender tails and away they fled.

One fellow darted to a hole at my feet, and vanished into his storage burrow. He reappeared in a trice, cheek pouches empty, and scampered up another rose bush. I watched them for at least a half an hour; not once did they pause in their activity. They seemed more spirit than earth.

Habitat

Prime habitat for the red-tailed chipmunk is the highland country, with islands of coniferous trees and rich undergrowth, such as rhododendron, heather, or blueberry bushes.

In Canada, he is found at altitudes from 1300 to 2400 m, on sunny slopes with scattered trees; in open valleys with stands of spruce, fir and pine; and among rock-pocked underbrush. He is not usually present at lower altitudes, and because of his arboreal nature he does not range above tree-line.

The red-tailed chipmunk, like the yellow-pine and least chipmunks, may occupy both subsurface dens and tree nests in the course of a year. Underground burrows are used for hibernation and as natal dens, but may be employed at any season. Tree nests are a temporary home for both sexes, and the young, during the summer months.

A typical tree-nest is a spherical ball of grass averaging 35 cm in diameter, which resembles a covered bird's nest. Arboreal nests are usually sited close to the tree trunk from 5 to 18 m above ground. Most are found in conifers such as the Engelmann spruce, Douglas fir, and lodgepole pine, although many are built in the branches of aspens. These nests are sometimes difficult to spot because they are often placed just below a patch of dense foliage or a clump of witches'-broom. It is likely chipmunks deliberately site their nests in the shadow of these clumps because they provide excellent camouflage and additional protection against the elements. Some arboreal nests are located in tall stumps and woodpecker holes.

Underground burrows may be dug in open ground, beneath a stump or windfall, or in a crevice among loose rocks. This type of dwelling has a well-disguised entrance tunnel, which leads to a single coconut-shaped chamber approximately 13 cm in diameter, roughly 28 cm below the surface.

Both tree nests and underground dens are snugly lined with dried grass and shredded vegetation. The red-tailed chipmunk likes to have a supply of food at hand; during the summer the amount may be minimal, but just prior to hibernation their larders are invariably well stocked.

Being diurnal, he may feed at any time during the day, but in normal weather the peak periods of activity are usually early in the morning and late in the afternoon. From August until hibernation, a significant portion of the non-perishable food gathered each day is used to stock his winter larder.

Feeding Habits

The red-tailed chipmunk is primarily herbivorous and feeds mainly on buds, seeds, fruits, leaves, and flowers. Less-important items in his diet are nuts, fungi, and animal matter in the form of insects and grubs. Both his appetite and his foraging habits are similar to the yellow-pine chipmunk's.

An interesting aspect of his feeding behaviour is the dexterity with which he handles large food items. Small seeds and buds are eaten with a minimum of preparation, but large objects, regardless of their texture, need to be manipulated in such a way as to present a surface to bite into. His technique is to rapidly rotate the bulky item in his paws until he finds an edge that he can grip with his upper incisors. Then, with the edge positioned against his upper teeth, he deftly rotates the object in his paws until he can bite off a chunk with his lower teeth. The fragment is allowed to fall to the ground and is subsequently eaten. When the small piece has been swallowed, he picks up his burden again and repeats the process. The whole procedure takes place so swiftly that an observer must watch closely to follow the steps.

Life Cycle

Red-tailed chipmunks emerge from hibernation in April or May, depending upon the latitude and the severity of the winter. Mating takes place shortly after emergence and the young are born in May or June, following a gestation period of approximately 30 days. Older females bear larger litters than those in their first breeding season; most mature females have 5 or 6 pups. The young are born beneath the ground, and are usually transferred to a tree nest in their fifth week. By this time their eyes have opened, their coats are well furred, and they have good coordination. During the weeks that the young family shares a tree nest, their mother leaves them on their own for several hours each day while she forages for herself. Her normal routine is to quietly leave the tree before sunup and to return around midmorning to suckle her babies. In the afternoon, she may make another feeding trip, while the young explore the terrain within 30 m of their home. The family often gathers near the nest to socialize for the half hour before sunset. At this time, the mother chipmunk will join in games with her babies, who particularly enjoy "rough and tumble", "chase", and "follow the leader". When the sun sets, the family quietly retires to their tree for the night. The young are weaned and disperse during August. In Canada, most red-tailed chipmunks enter hibernation during October and November. Like other members of the squirrel family, the young of the year are the last to go below ground.

Red-tailed chipmunks spend the winter months in hibernation. Their hibernating dens are normally located beneath the ground and are lined with grass, lichen, and other insulating materials such as thistledown, feathers, and animal hair. In the weeks prior to hibernation, they cache a great many seeds in their sleeping chambers. When they enter their hibernaculum for the winter, they plug the entrance tunnel with earth or matted vegetation. This helps to protect them from predators and keeps the snow out. Then they curl into a ball and drift into a torpor, which is accompanied by a dramatic slowdown in their respiration, heartbeat, and metabolism. They may rouse from this sleep periodically every ten days or so to eat and perform bodily functions. The supply of cached, non-perishable food supplies their needs until they emerge in spring.

This species has a relatively long life-span. If they survive their juvenile year—and many don't—they have a reasonable chance of living for another 4 years.

Natural Enemies

The most dangerous predator of the red-tailed chipmunk is the long-tailed weasel. Weasels are swift on the ground and excellent climbers; in many instances, they are slender enough to follow a chipmunk into his den. Bobcats and coyotes also prey on the red-tailed chipmunk as do rattlesnakes (in the few Canadian regions where their ranges overlap). Because of his diminutive size, he is vulnerable to both hawks and the diurnal Pygmy Owl.

This species, like all western chipmunks, is afflicted by numerous parasites in the form of fleas, ticks, lice, and mites. He is particularly victimized by the botfly larva, which penetrates his skin, and by several types of tapeworm, which can live in his intestines.

Relations with Humans

The red-tailed chipmunk has a small range in Canada, restricted to the uninhabited regions of the Selkirk and Rocky mountains. Thus Man has had little influence on his distribution and abundance.

Although he is a delightful member of the wildlife community, he is of no economic importance.

Where to Observe

Because of his remote habitat, most red-tailed chipmunks are seen only by hikers when they pause to rest or picnic in the shade of a coniferous grove. Listen for his *chirp*, and watch for a flash of movement in the lower branches.

Grey or Black Squirrel
Écureuil gris ou noir
Sciurus carolinensis

Common Names

In most instances, he is simply called a grey squirrel. However, because of the high percentage of melanistic animals, especially in Canada, he is also known as a black squirrel. Indeed, many people believe that black squirrels are a separate species rather than a colour phase of the grey. For simplicity, I have referred to him as a grey squirrel throughout the text.

His scientific name, *Sciurus carolinensis*, refers both to his plume-like tail, and the locality where he was first identified. *Sciurus* comes from the Greek and means "creature who sits in the shadow of his tail", while *carolinensis* is the Latinized name for the original state of Carolina.

Description

The grey squirrel has a slender body, short curved claws, and a long flowing tail. He is a typical example of the tree squirrel, and is a familiar sight to most Canadians. His colouring may be grey, dark brown or black, red-brown, or pure white, but his most common colouring is grey or black. Grey squirrels dominate the south and central part of the range, while blacks often outnumber greys in the north. Red or white specimens are unusual, although there are a few small pockets of albino animals in the United States, the largest being near the town of Olney, Illinois. This colony is said to have sprung from a pair of albinos kept by a local saloon keeper in the 1870s.

When seen at a distance, grey squirrels appear beige-grey, and their tail has a luminous white border. The salt-and-pepper shade of their coat is owing to dense-grey underfur, overlaid by brown-banded guard hairs; the halo effect of their tail is created by silver-tipped guard hairs. Their face and paws are light brown; they have a white eye-ring, and white underparts. Their winter coat has a dominant beige dorsal stripe.

Melanistic squirrels are usually solid black, although some have rust-coloured fur, or a white tip, on their tails.

The grey squirrel moults twice each year; in spring and in autumn. All his fur is replaced in the spring moult, which commences at his head; the autumn moult moves in the opposite direction, and excludes his tail. The average weight for this species is 510 g, and his overall length—half being his tail—is approximately 50 cm.

Grey or Black Squirrel

Canadian Range

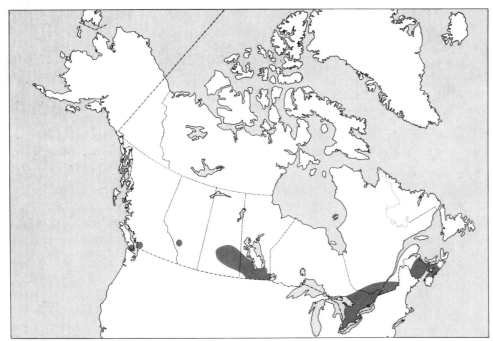

Range

Southern Ontario is the northern extremity of this species' natural range, which coincides with the deciduous forests. In the past 50 years, grey squirrels have spread into the southern portions of New Brunswick, Quebec, and Manitoba. Others have been introduced to Nova Scotia, as well as urban areas in Saskatchewan, Alberta, and British Columbia, including the Nanaimo region on Vancouver Island. Several of the Maritime squirrel colonies are believed to have immigrated accidentally from central Canada, by hopping aboard grain cars bound for the eastern seaboard.

Population density varies with the terrain; suitable habitat usually holds one squirrel per hectare.

Behaviour

Even though the grey squirrel is well known in eastern Canada, he is still surrounded by folklore. The popular misconception that grey and black squirrels are two separate species often leads to a second false conclusion—that greys dominate blacks, or vice versa. At the risk of labouring the point, both are colour phases of the same species. Another myth says that he is bullied by his cousin the red squirrel (*Tamiasciurus hudsonicus*), who frequently castrates him in combat. The grain of truth in this story is that the grey is tolerant, and permits the red squirrel to enforce his territorial rights without opposition. However, the grey will trespass whenever he pleases, and usually suffers nothing worse than a scolding as punishment.

The grey is a sociable animal who lives in loose groupings and exhibits little agonistic behaviour. There is a pecking order, normally headed by an old male, but dominance is characterized by chasing and a show of strength rather than vicious fighting. He is diurnal; his most active periods of the day are early morning and mid-afternoon, although it is not unusual to see him flitting through tree branches on a moonlit night. He is alert and agile, spending much of his time in the trees, which he climbs and descends head first. His top speed on the ground is approximately 24 km/h, but he has extraordinary mobility, and can change direction in a flash. When hiding in a tree, he often freezes against the bark, or quietly slides around the trunk to keep out of sight of a pursuer. He can perform amazing feats aloft, such as running along a swaying telephone wire while carrying a load of three butternuts, each the size of a ping-pong ball. The secret of his balance is his long bushy tail, which acts as a balancing staff. He spends a great deal of time grooming his tail, for it also serves a number of other valuable purposes, acting as a parachute, a signal flag, a sunshade/umbrella, and a warm wrap. Like the ground squirrels, the grey squirrel has exquisite muscular control over his tail, which he can twist in any direction, as well as elevating or depressing its long guard hairs.

The normal call of the grey squirrel is a series of rasping *whicks*; when he is agitated, his scolding has a clicking sound. Female greys have a peculiar mating call, similar to the quacking of a duck, which is used to announce they are in heat. The effect of this call is electric, and it may summon as many as a dozen suitors who chase her through the trees. Initially she spurns them all, but eventually accepts one. Their pairing is brief, and the male leaves her minutes after the event.

This species has a well-developed homing instinct, which permits it to forage far from home if necessary. A few years ago I resorted to live-trapping grey squirrels in my garden and transporting them to a park beside the Ottawa River, a distance of roughly 3 km. The number of squirrels failed to diminish. Then I recognized two that I had "deported" and realized that all I had done was to give them some exercise!

Early naturalists named this species *Sciurus migratorus* because in the 1800s there were remarkable movements of grey squirrels from one locality to another. These were immigrations rather than migrations, since the animals did not return to their original starting point.

Well-documented accounts tell of hundreds of thousands descending like locusts on the settlers' fields in Ohio and Pennsylvania. The reason for these mass movements is unclear, but most authorities believe that they were triggered by a "population explosion" rather than famine or other natural aberration in the area. The only Canadian record of this phenomenon is in Seton's *Lives of Game Animals*, which tells of a horde that emigrated from southern Ontario to the United States:

. . . *innumerable Squirrels swam across the river Niagara and landed near Buffalo, New York, in such a state of exhaustion that the boys caught them in their hands, or knocked them from the fences and bushes with poles.*

There have been no significant squirrel migrations in the past 50 years because their numbers and their habitat have been sharply reduced.

Personality

The author, Richard Mathews, tells in his book, *Wild Animals as Pets*, about a grey squirrel named Peter, who lived with a women in New York.

Peter is an alert, active animal, more interesting and apparently more intelligent than most rodents. He comes when called—eventually—even when he is outside in the backyard making the acquaintance of a wild squirrel. His sensitivity is indicated by his reaction to Mrs. D'Essen when she, growing impatient with his antics, caught him in a towel and carried him brusquely back to his cage. He sulked in a corner and cried his high-pitched cry when she opened the cage and presented her hands for him to climb up on. A whole week went by before this how-could-you-have-done-such-a-thing-to-me? attitude softened. Peter is both sociable and gentle toward humans; he never bites unless frightened, and in all his eight years with Mrs. D'Essen the worst damage he has inflicted on her has been occasional stocking runs produced en route to his perch on her shoulders. . . .

Peter caches not only nuts but also such treasures as fountain pens, lipsticks and keys. Fond of cosmetic scents, he once secreted a compact. Mrs. D'Essen looked high and low for it until one day she caught Peter with the goods on his person, that is, with a heavily powdered face. She soon discovered where it was hidden.

Habitat

The natural habitat of the grey squirrel is a dense stand of mature hardwoods. In these surroundings, the tall deciduous trees have an ample crown of foliage, which offers protection against intense sunlight and high winds, as well as producing nuts and seeds for the squirrels to feed upon.

In urban areas, greys gravitate to the suburbs and parks with good-sized trees. The average territory for this species throughout its continental range is approximately 1 ha, although squirrels introduced to Stanley Park in British Columbia cover as much as 20 ha.

Grey squirrels occupy two types of home, both sited 9 to 12 m above ground. Their winter retreat, and natal den, is usually a cavity in the trunk of a hardwood tree; their summer home is often a nest of leaves and twigs in the branches of an elm, pine, or hemlock tree.

Den cavities are formed by the stump of a broken limb rotting into the trunk, or by woodpeckers. In either case, the squirrel must shape the entrance and modify the interior cavity with his teeth. Tree nests, or dreys, look like a ragged crow's-nest, but considerable skill is used to build them on a sturdy platform of twigs, with a waterproof exterior of leaves, and snug interior lined with shredded vegetation.

During the course of the summer, a family of squirrels sometimes occupies several dreys; in the winter it is common for several adults, or a mother and her young, to share the same tree cavity.

Feeding Habits

When searching for food on the ground, this species traces a random pattern in a series of hops, pausing from time to time to sit up with a twitch of his tail and check his bearings. Once he gets an edible morsel, he deals with it deftly using both his paws and teeth. When feeding in the trees, he often makes quite a clatter, and strews the ground with twigs and leaves. His ingenuity at getting around obstacles is well known to home gardeners, especially those who plant spring bulbs.

Grey squirrels are omnivores, whose staple food is nuts; but they eat a tremendous number of other items, and their menu is strongly influenced by the season. In early spring, they subsist on the buds of hardwoods, switching to the samaras and flowers of the same trees as the season advances. In summer, they have a wide choice of fruits and berries, and they may also eat animal matter in the form of grasshoppers, caterpillars, and birds' eggs. The best feeding time is autumn when, in a good year, the trees are laden with nuts and acorns. Some of this bounty is consumed, but many nuts are cached. Because they are industrious hoarders, they become thoroughly engrossed with their task, and frequently seem oblivious to the hazards of traffic. From the beginning of September, many are killed by cars when they attempt to cross busy streets. Winter is a harsh survival test. By the first week in January, their buried larder is empty and to live, they are forced to eat pine seeds, buds, twigs, and bark. Even squirrels in the city feel the pinch of hunger at this time, and resort to raiding bird feeders. One solution to this problem is to place the feeding tray on a post that has a disc-shaped cone of metal between the tray and the ground. This arrangement prevents most squirrels from reaching the seed, and the birds, particularly Grosbeaks, will fling enough food off the tray so that both parties have sufficient to eat.

A high percentage of nuts buried in autumn are never recovered and eventually take root. Thus the grey squirrel makes an important contribution to the renewal of the trees upon which he feeds.

Life Cycle

Although grey squirrels are poly-oestrous and capable of producing two litters each year (in late winter and mid-summer) most bear only one litter. Mating takes place around the end of January, and the babies are born in March, following a gestation period of 44 days. An average litter contains 3 pups, each weighing approximately 16 g at birth. The grey is a solicitous mother, who guards her offspring closely and will move them at the first sign of danger, holding each baby by the skin of its belly, and wearing it like a ruff around her neck. At the age of 5 weeks, the little ones open their eyes; 2 weeks later they are weaned. By the time they are 2 months old, they have increased their birth weight tenfold, and are foraging for themselves. Most juvenile males and some females disperse in the autumn, and many fall victim to predators, cars, hunters, or starvation. The mortality rate among first-year animals is estimated to run as high as 75 per cent of the total born. Those that survive will be fully mature the following spring.

The grey squirrel does not hibernate, even though he puts on a substantial layer of fat in autumn. He will, however, ride out a blizzard, or a severe cold snap, by staying in his den for several days at a time.

The maximum life expectancy in the wild for this species is estimated to be around 6 years, although some have lived to twice this age in captivity.

Natural Enemies

Grey squirrels have a host of enemies. They are preyed upon by weasels, foxes, bobcats, raccoons, skunks, and snakes. Hawks also take their toll, particularly the Red-tailed, Cooper's, and Goshawk. Although this squirrel is diurnal, he occasionally remains out after dark, and is sometimes snatched by a Great Horned Owl.

Like the other Sciuridae, the grey squirrel is afflicted by parasites such as fleas, mites, ticks, and the larva of the botfly warble, which lodges in the groinal region. Botfly warbles are severely debilitating, while the scabies mite, which causes mange and loss of fur, can bring about death by exposure.

Relations with Humans

We have reduced the natural habitat of the grey squirrel by cutting down much of the hardwood forest, and we have thinned his ranks with guns and automobiles.

Those we "protect" in parks and cities often degenerate into freeloading nuisances who bear little resemblance to their brothers in the wild. Tests have proved that peanuts, the staple "handout", contain insufficient nourishment to keep squirrels in good health.

The grey squirrel is an important small-game animal throughout the United States and in part of Ontario; the annual kill in Florida exceeds 1.5 million squirrels. His pelt has no commercial value—except for his tail, which is used in the manufacture of fishing lures—but his flesh is edible, and squirrel pie is considered a delicacy by many people.

He is not a serious agricultural pest, for the harm he does to crops and gardens is more than offset by the hardwood trees he inadvertently "plants".

The grey squirrel occupies an unusual niche in American history. Being a small and elusive target, he is credited with making the early settlers crack shots, and thereby contributing to the defeat of the British in the American Revolution. Ernest Thompson Seton supported this premise, and cited another example from the Civil War: in 1862, when Ohio was threatened by Confederate troops, 50,000 men volunteered with their long rifles and were officially known as the Squirrel Hunters.

Where to Observe
This typical tree squirrel is easily observed at close quarters in parks or well-treed urban areas throughout his range.

Fox Squirrel
Écureuil fauve
Sciurus niger

Common Names
Most often, he is simply called a fox squirrel. However, in the southern part of his range, where red and melanistic strains are common, he is also known as a big red squirrel, or a white-nosed black squirrel.

His scientific name, *Sciurus niger*, is derived in part from the Greek words *skia* meaning "shadow", and *oura* meaning "tail". *Sciurus* is the Latin transliteration for *skia* and *oura*, and may be freely translated as "creature who sits in the shadow of his tail". *Niger*, Latin for "black", refers to his melanistic phase.

Description
Although he is the largest and most heavyset of our tree dwellers, the fox squirrel is sometimes mistaken at a distance for his cousins the grey squirrel or the red squirrel. The reason for this confusion is that the fox squirrel has three distinct colour phases—black, beige-grey, and red. Unlike the grey squirrel, melanistic fox squirrels have a white nose and ears, while those in the red phase differ from the red squirrel because their underparts are dark buff rather than white.

Most fox squirrels in Canada and the northern part of the continent are beige-grey. In this phase, their head, back, and sides are dun-coloured; their ears, cheeks, and feet ochreous; and their underparts tawny. Their luxuriant tails have a mottled black-and-orange pattern above, with a copper-coloured underside.

The overall length for both sexes is approximately 54 cm, with the average weight being around 800 g. It is interesting to note that the largest fox-squirrel skin in the collection of the National Museum of Natural Sciences was collected by Ernest Thompson Seton in 1899. It is 61 cm long, and was taken from a female who weighed a whopping 1116 g.

This species moults once a year, in April or May. The new fur progresses from the region of the head and shoulders toward the tail.

Fox Squirrel

Range

Fox squirrels were introduced to Canada (on Pelee Island, Ontario) in 1893 by an American, Charles Mills, who obtained his stock from southern Ohio near the Kentucky border. Over thirty years later, Dr. Hoyes Lloyd sadly reported in the *Canadian Field-Naturalist* that the fox squirrel had been exterminated from Pelee Island because of over-shooting. Fortunately, this grim news was premature; a few squirrels managed to survive in a remote part of the island. Today, the population is estimated to be between 200 and 300 animals.

The continental range of the fox squirrel follows the edge of the hardwood forest. During the last 100 years, they have extended their territory to the north and west. For this reason, Minnesota and the Dakotas have growing populations, and there are signs that the species is moving into several parts of Canada. Recently, fox squirrels have been reported in the Niagara Glen region of southern Ontario, and at least two have been found dead on roads near Winnipeg, Manitoba.

Population density varies with the habitat. In prime cover, there may be as many as 5 adults to the hectare; however, on Pelee Island, the animals are widely dispersed and a 20 ha woodlot may only hold 5 or 6.

Canadian Range

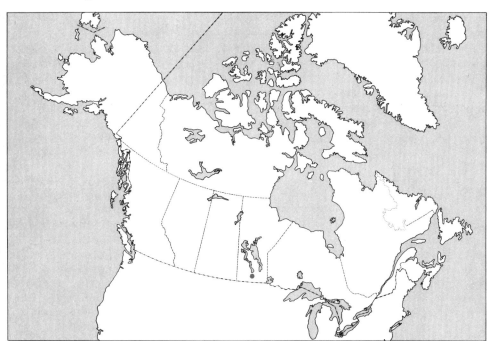

Behaviour

The fox squirrel lives a solitary life, although the home range of one may overlap the home range of another, and it is not unusual for several to spend the winter in the same tree. He is strictly diurnal, rising well after sunup and returning to shelter before dark. Ernest Thompson Seton noted in *Lives of Game Animals:*

Ten or eleven in the morning is the favourite time with him. Forth he comes in that bright hot spell; and, for four or five hours, prowls and plays the life game with the fullest measure of his gifts. Then, as definitely, he retires to rest, as though he meant to avoid meeting that Grey-squirrel crowd, with their vulgar levity and unrestraint.

This tree squirrel frequently travels long distances on the ground; on Pelee Island, he may leave his woodlot and range several hundred metres into a cornfield. During the mating season in late winter, males have been known to journey 30 km in search of a mate. He is also a good climber, who can easily leap 2 m from one limb to another. At the approach of danger, he will sometimes drop from his tree and try to outrun the intruder; at other times he will try to escape through the treetops, jumping from branch to branch. Even when an observer suspects he is in a certain tree, he can be difficult to spot because he will keep on the far side of the trunk. When the observer changes position, so will he.

The call of the fox squirrel, a metallic *chick chick*, is similar to that of the grey squirrel, except the first of the two notes is high-pitched, and he doesn't chatter and scold as much as the grey.

His tail, the longest and bushiest of the Canadian Sciuridae, has many uses. It serves as a sunshade when he sprawls on his stomach at midday; an umbrella when he squats on a limb in the rain; a signal flag to complement his call; a balancing staff for aerial footwork; a shield in combat; and a parachute that permits him to fall five stories without injury.

Like the other tree squirrels, he is an inveterate hoarder of nuts, but his recovery rate is better than that of his cousins. In tests, he was retrieved nearly 100 per cent of the nuts he buried. Most authorities attribute this phenomenal talent to a combination of memory and a keen nose —mostly the latter. He needs to have water on a regular basis, and may drink (by sucking rather than lapping) daily.

These squirrels seem to posess a mild temperament for there is little strife among families, and they can live in harmony with the red and the grey squirrels. However, female fox squirrels guard their natal dens bravely against all comers, and both sexes will fight courageously when cornered by a much-larger opponent, such as a dog or a cat.

Personality

Ernest Thompson Seton maintained that the fox squirrel could make a safe and gentle pet, and mentioned that he had known several who were "ideally tame and kind". To support his theory, Seton quoted another prominent Canadian naturalist, P.A. Taverner:

P.A. Taverner, of Ottawa, tells me that he knew the Fox-squirrel very well during his years of residence in Michigan; and considers it far more easily tamed, and much more intelligent than the gray. Late one winter, about 1912, at Ann Arbor, Mich., he saw an amusing sight that illustrates the disposition of the Fox-squirrel. Near the campus of the University, was a little girl sitting in the porch of her home; she was feeding a lot of Fox-squirrels. Nine were scrambling all over her at once, as she cracked walnuts and hickory nuts with a hammer to feed them. She could scarcely keep from cracking their heads, they crowded in so closely, and were so eager to seize every nut as soon as it was available. Those that could not get on her lap, went through her pockets.

Habitat

The favourite haunt of the fox squirrel is a stand of tall hardwood trees on the edge of a forest. Normally, he avoids dense woods because he likes to be adjacent to open country. This combination of terrain provides him with food, shelter, and good visibility to spot the approach of enemies.

On Pelee Island, these squirrels are found close to farms in stands of oak and hickory; along tall hedgerows; and in large woodlots. Near the Manitoba border, they favour isolated groves surrounded by grainfields.

Population density is determined by the forest type. In the southern part of their range, oak and hickory are prime cover and may support as may as five adults to the hectare. A poor nut crop, or extensive predation, can force these squirrels to move, or seriously reduce their numbers.

Fox squirrels usually site their home in a hardwood tree, approximately 10 m above ground. During the course of a year, they may move several times, and occupy two distinctly different structures. Normally, their natal den (and winter residence) is a cavity in the trunk of a tree, while their summer home may be a nest of twigs perched among its branches. Both nests are lined with shredded vegetation.

A squirrel nest is deceptive because it looks like a ragged ball of foliage that would disintegrate in the first light breeze. In fact, it is firmly secured in the fork of the limb and well engineered; most can withstand a gale. Nests used for resting, or temporary residence, are often open above, like a crow's nest. More-permanent nests are enclosed, with a single entrance, and have the added virtue of being rainproof.

Dens in the trunk of a tree are formed when a shaded limb breaks off, and the dead stub conducts moisture inside the trunk, causing decay. The fox squirrel then gnaws around the opening, and clears out the rotten wood. Tree dens provide the best protection against the elements and enemies; some have been used for fifty years. It is worth mentioning that these dens are formed in mature trees that have usually been damaged by time and weather; thus squirrel excavations cause no harm to the sound trees in a woodlot.

Both the latitude and the terrain affect the choice of a home. On Pelee Island, there are few nests because most of the fox-squirrel population live in oak and hickory cavities throughout the year.

Feeding Habits

The fox squirrel is an omnivore, whose diet consists primarily of buds, seeds, flowers, berries, and nuts. Like other squirrels, he will occasionally eat animal matter such as grubs, insects, caterpillars, and birds' eggs. He requires liquid each day, which he obtains by eating fruits and berries, by licking dew off foliage, or by sucking water from streams and puddles.

During late summer, this species spends a lot of time harvesting and then caching acorns and nuts. These staples are buried individually, to a depth of around 4 cm, and are retrieved during autumn and winter. Fox squirrels have a well-developed sense of smell that allows them to locate nuts even when they are covered by both earth and a layer of snow.

Their menu changes with the calendar. In spring, they rely on buried nuts, plus the seeds and samaras of oak, maple, elm, and hickory trees. In summer, they have a broad choice of flowers and fruits including strawberries, raspberries, chokecherries, blueberries, and grapes. Other additions to their diet at this time are insects and caterpillars and, if they live near a cornfield, corn niblets in the "milk" stage—the last being a very special delicacy. Autumn is the time of plenty; in a good year, nuts and acorns are everywhere. In winter, they must rely on their buried hoard, augmented if necessary by hawthorn berries, rose-hips and scattered seeds.

Life Cycle

Although fox squirrels are poly-oestrous, mating twice annually (in January/February and May/June), most females only bear one litter each year. In the mating season, several males may court the same female, but there is usually a single pairing. The young are born after a gestation period of 44 days. Most litters consist of 3 blind and hairless pups, each weighing approximately 15 g, with an overall length of 10 cm.

A mother fox-squirrel is fiercely protective of her young, chasing everyone (including her mate) away from the natal den. Should she become concerned for the safety of her pups, she will not hesitate to carry them, one at a time, to a new home. Her babies open their eyes at 6 weeks and taste their first solid food a few days later. At this age, they are quite active in the den, and begin to explore the outside world under their mother's close supervision. They are not completely weaned until their third month, but once they are weaned, they are on their own. Most youngsters leave the natal den in autumn, and some males travel up to 30 km before establishing their own home. Others spend the first winter with their mother, and disperse as yearlings. Females reach sexual maturity the following spring, well ahead of their male littermates, who don't mate until they are two years old.

Fox squirrels put on weight in autumn, but they do not hibernate. In the southern part of their range, they stay active all winter. In the northern area, including Pelee Island, they often remain in their dens for several consecutive days during severe weather. Throughout the range, their favourite winter home is a snug cavity in an oak or hickory tree. It is not unusual for more than one squirrel to occupy a den—either a pair of adults, or a mother with her young.

Once the snow comes, they make frequent trips to retrieve their hoard of nuts and acorns. Often their larder is bare by the end of January, and they are forced to eat buds and seeds. Midwinter is a grim period for all but the fittest.

Fox squirrel populations fluctuate from year to year especially when subjected to severe human or natural predation, a nut-crop failure, or disease. Fortunately, Nature compensates to some extent during these declines by increasing the litter size of the survivors. Individual animals have a maximum life expectancy in the wild of approximately 8 years.

Natural Enemies

The most dangerous predator is the Red-tailed Hawk. Owls, being nocturnal hunters, are not a serious menace. On land, foxes, raccoons, dogs, and domestic cats all take their toll.

This species is host to a variety of ticks, mites, and fleas; the scabies mite *Sarcoptes* is one of the worst because it causes a mange-like condition that can lead to death through debilitation and exposure.

Relations with Humans

Over the past century, the habitat of the fox squirrel in the United States has been drastically reduced by the felling of many oak and hardwood stands. In some areas, he has been totally eliminated. The automobile accounts for an increasing number of deaths each year, while the annual hunter kill is measured in the hundreds of thousands.

The first Canadian colony was almost exterminated by overshooting. Today on Pelee Island, this large and relatively slow-moving squirrel is still subject to excessive hunting pressure near corn cribs and in isolated groves.

The fox squirrel is a popular target for small-game hunters because of his size and edible flesh. His pelt has no commercial value, except for the hairs of his tail, which are used in the manufacture of certain fishing lures.

His taste for young corn qualifies him as a pest to farmers although, in practice, the culprits are so few in number they rarely cause noticeable damage.

In 1929, Ernest Thompson Seton wrote:

The Fox-squirrel is, in some respects, the highest product of evolution in the Squirrel family. It is our largest, most specialized, most variably coloured Squirrel. But in some matters, it is far behind the time; and so badly equipped for the life-struggle that we do not wonder at its disappearance from a large part of its range.

Where to Observe

In Canada, the best place to observe the fox-squirrel is on Pelee Island, Ontario. Favourite habitat is an isolated grove of bur oak, although he will also show himself near a well-stocked corn crib.

Walk quietly, and remember that he will try to stay on the opposite side of the tree trunk, away from observers.

American Red Squirrel
Écureuil roux
Tamiasciurus hudsonicus

Common Names

Most of us know this species as the common or American red squirrel. Because of his garrulous nature, he is also called a barking squirrel, and his preference for coniferous trees has earned him the nickname, pine squirrel. He is the squirrel named Adjidomo in Long-fellow's epic poem *Hiawatha*.

His formal designation, *Tamiasciurus hudsonicus*, is most descriptive: *Tamiasciurus* is Latin meaning "the steward who sits in the shadow of his tail", while *hudsonicus* refers to Hudson Bay, the locality where this species was first catalogued in 1771 by the German naturalist Jean Erxleben.

Description

The American red squirrel is easy to identify because he is smaller and chunkier than the grey squirrel, but almost twice the size of the largest chipmunk. At first glance, he appears to be brown above and white below. This is deceiving because he moults twice each year and wears two distinct coats, with the only constant coloration being his white eye-ring and tawny tail.

In summer, his sides and back have a dark-olive cast, while his head, rump, and legs are various shades of brown. His throat and underparts are white. The contrast between the dark and light fur is heightened by a black lateral stripe.

In winter, the rufous colour in his tail spreads along his back. His head, sides, and rump range in tone from beige to chestnut, the black lateral stripe fades away, and his underparts change to a silvery-grey.

The average overall length for this species is 31 cm, and adults of both sexes weigh approximately 230 g. Albino or melanistic red squirrels are rarely encountered.

American Red Squirrel

Canadian Range

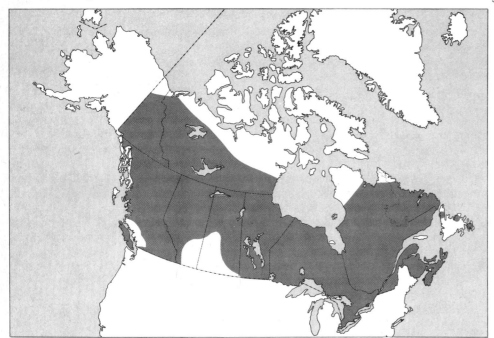

Range

The American red squirrel has a gigantic range, and is found in all the provinces, as well as in the Northwest Territories. This includes Newfoundland, where he was introduced to the Hare Bay region in 1963 by local fishermen, who brought several pairs across the Strait of Belle Isle from Labrador. These immigrants have flourished and are presently spreading through the northern peninsula.

Population density varies with the latitude and the terrain. Prime habitat may host as many as five squirrels to the hectare but the average is probably closer to one for every 2 ha.

Behaviour

The American red squirrel is a noisy little extrovert with enormous energy. He is not communal, but he will sometimes share his den with a mate, or engage in play with other red squirrels. Frequently, however, what we perceive to be a game of "tag" may in reality be a serious chase, for he has a strong sense of territory. This species has a personal territory because it is the best way for him to protect his food supply. Any poacher entering his domain, be it another red squirrel, a grey squirrel, a Crow, or a Jay, is greeted with a string of abuse and immediately given chase. Fortunately, few of these encounters result in bloodshed, because, as a general rule, interlopers are inclined to retreat rather than to fight. Grey squirrels often share the same habitat as the red squirrel, and are frequent trespassers. The common sight of a red squirrel chasing a grey may have led to the belief that he castrates his larger cousin. In fact, the two rarely engage in physical combat.

The American red squirrel is diurnal. His activities coincide with the most comfortable hours of the season—early morning and late afternoon in the summer, midday in the winter. During the nut-gathering weeks of September, he will sometimes continue his work by moonlight.

These squirrels are nimble and daring climbers who can run at full speed on the underside of a limb, or jump several metres to an adjacent tree. Occasionally their confidence exceeds their ability, and they fall. In this event, they adopt a spread-eagled position (which slows their descent), or they try to catch a branch on the way down. Both procedures work; some red squirrels have dropped more than 30 m without injury. On the ground, they try to chart their course in a series of laps from the base of one tree to another, and usually move at a gallop. This strategy makes them an elusive quarry for land-bound predators. All the Sciuridae are competent swimmers, but the red squirrel, who swims with his head and tail out of the water, is renowned for making long-distance journeys. These marathon swims are not without hazard; some of the travellers end up in the stomachs of pike, muskellunge, and lake trout.

The American red squirrel is a chatterbox who seems to delight in the sound of his own voice. This trait has earned him the Latin name *loquax* (which means loquacious), as well as the nicknames chickaree, boomer, and barking squirrel. His frequently heard territorial call is a rolling *Chrrrrr*, which sounds like a ratchet. Should his curiosity be aroused, he will study the situation and make soft *whuck whuck* noises. When he is angry or agitated he jerks his tail, stamps his feet, and scolds with a penetrating *Tchrrrrr*.

He is also noted for his industry and intelligence in the procurement of food. Fruits, cones, and nuts are harvested at just the right stage of their development, and cached on the basis of their perishability; hard foods go below ground, and soft foods above ground. Despite the range of hiding places, his memory, combined with his nose, permits him to retrieve a high percentage of these items. In the dead of winter, when food is scarce, he will tunnel under the snow to tap his buried larder or to reach distant food sources. Although the red squirrel is a sloppy housekeeper, he is fastidious concerning his personal cleanliness. Whenever he has been eating greasy food, digging, or handling a sticky cone, he washes his paws with his tongue, then grooms the rest of his coat with his paws,except for his tail which he "combs" with his teeth.

A number of authorities on squirrel behaviour, including Dr. A. Brooker Klugh, Queen's University, Kingston, have concluded that this little rodent possesses not only a keen mind, but the ability to reason on a primary level.

Personality

Following an expedition to the Adirondacks in the 1880s, Clinton Merriam, a prominent American zoologist and physician, had this to say about the red squirrel:

The Chickaree combines qualities so wholly at variance, so unique, so incomprehensible, and so characteristic withal, that one scarcely knows in what light to regard him. His inquisitiveness, audacity, inordinate assurance, and exasperating insolence, together with his insatiable love of mischief and shameless disregard of all the ordinary customs and civilities of life, would lead one to suppose that he was little entitled to respect; and yet his intelligence, his untiring perseverance, and genuine industry, the cunning cleverness displayed in many of his actions and the irresistible humour with which he does everything command for him a certain degree of admiration. He is arrogant, impetuous, and conceited to an extreme degree, his confidence in his own superior capabilities not infrequently costing him his life. In fact, these contradictions in character and idiosyncrasies in disposition render him a psychological problem of no easy solution.

Habitat

The American red squirrel has managed to adapt to a variety of terrain across Canada, which is one of the secrets of his survival. His primary habitat, which he invariably occupies when given the choice, is coniferous forest, especially spruce and pine trees. Secondary habitat consists of mixed hardwoods, particularly stands of maple and elm.

The average territory, or home range, for an individual animal is 0.75 ha.

His usual home is a cavity in the trunk of a tree, or a leaf-and-twig nest among its branches. However, he will sometimes take up residence in a jumble of logs, a rotten stump, a pile of stones, or in northern areas, in a tunnel in the snow.

Given a choice, he prefers to use a tree cavity as a natal den. These cavities are formed by the decayed stump of a branch, and the hole is gnawed to a suitable size by the squirrel. Another source of shelter is an unused woodpecker hole.

Both types of cavity are lined with shredded vegetation to make a snug chamber.

Tree nests or dreys are used throughout the range during the summer, and are the main tree-home in coniferous forests. Dreys have a single entrance, and are firmly anchored in the branches or against the trunk; sometimes the foundation is the old nest of a crow or hawk. Although the nests have a scruffy appearance because the outer layer is composed of coarse twigs and leaves, the weather-repellent outer shell hides an inner lining of fine bark-fibres or other soft vegetable material.

Feeding Habits

American red squirrels are primarily seed and nut eaters, but they can live on a wide assortment of vegetable and animal matter. Much of their time is spent gathering and storing food, a task they execute with surprising efficiency. Cones are harvested while they are still green, which ensures that the seeds remain in place. Ten to a dozen cones are cut at one time before the squirrel descends the tree to prepare them for storage by stripping away the excess material. Some of the cones are buried, the rest are distributed in little piles around his territory. Many of these cache locations are used by generations of squirrels, and can be easily spotted by the refuse pile, or midden, of husks, which may cover more than 1 m^2 to a depth of 7 cm. Nonperishable items such as nuts and seeds are usually buried, while soft foods such as fruits and mushrooms are carefully lodged in the branches of trees.

In good crop years, the squirrels usually cache far more than they need. Brooker Klugh told of two friends in Frontenac County, Ontario, who stumbled upon a squirrel's hoard of butternuts in a hollow tree. The men proceeded to fill a bushel-and-a-half bag with nuts, and left the bag near the tree, intending to return with a wheelbarrow the next morning. That night the squirrel found the bag, chewed a hole in the bottom, and removed all the nuts to a more secure hiding-place.

In winter, red squirrels depend upon their autumn larder. When the snow comes, they often dig tunnels to get at this underground storehouse. Another important use for their tunnels is to reach food sources in exposed locations. Last January, I noticed a 5 cm hole in the snow at the base of the post-mounted bird feeder in the centre of my lawn. The next day I saw a red squirrel pop out of the hole and quickly eat the seeds that had fallen from the feeding tray. He may have been a juvenile, because he didn't seem to mind sharing his "territory" with a number of grey squirrels, and he often fed peacefully within inches of them.

In the early spring, the squirrels supplement their diet with the buds of leaves and flowers as well as bark and samaras.

During this season, they relish the sap of the sugar maple and sweet birch, which they obtain by biting through the bark, or by tapping holes bored by sapsuckers.

In the summer, they eat a wide assortment of foods such as flowers, fruits, seeds and mushrooms, as well as insects, grubs, birds' eggs and fledglings. By the end of summer they have come full circle, and their entire attention is occupied with collecting nuts and cones for the winter.

Squirrel populations in the northern coniferous regions are subject to severe fluctuations directly tied to the annual cone crop; populations to the south are more stable because they are not so heavily dependent upon a single food source.

Life Cycle

Because red squirrels are polyoestrous, they are capable of bearing two litters each year. However, throughout most of Canada, the temperate season is so short that they only have one litter annually, in spring. Their mating takes place about the time of the first major thaws, which occur across the country from the end of February to the beginning of April.

Most squirrels are born during April and May after a gestation period of 35 days. The average litter size is 4 pups, each weighing around 7 g. At birth, they are totally helpless and look, in the words of an early naturalist, "absurd, like miniature pug dogs, blind and naked with enormous heads". Within a few weeks they are covered with downy fur, and their eyes open by the end of their first month. They are weaned at 8 weeks, but stay in their mother's care until the end of the summer. Many juveniles disperse in September, although some families share the natal den for the first winter. Young squirrels become fully mature as yearlings.

Red squirrels appear unperturbed by low temperatures and are frequently active when the thermometer registers –25°C. However they will remain in their den for several days during the height of a severe blizzard, or during periods of extreme cold.

The average life-span for this species is estimated to be less than 3 years; approximately 70 per cent of the juveniles die during their first winter. This high mortality rate is mainly caused by starvation, as few juveniles are able to establish a territory, and thus they lack a reliable food supply. Captive red squirrels have lived for more than a dozen years.

Natural Enemies

The red squirrel is eaten by a number of carnivores, but especially by the pine marten, who has the speed and agility to catch him in the treetops. Other land predators are the fisher, mink, weasel, lynx, and bobcat. His main airborne enemies are the Goshawk, Red-shouldered Hawk, Sharp-shinned Hawk, and Sparrow Hawk. Owls take the occasional red squirrel, but are not a serious factor because most owls are nocturnal hunters.

This species suffers from parasites in the form of fleas, ticks, and mites. One of the most devastating natural disasters for squirrels living in coniferous forests is the failure of the cone crop; two consecutive bad years can reduce their numbers by 80 per cent. Forest fires are another terrible scourge, as these rodents don't run from the flames but climb a tree for safety.

Relations with Humans

The human influence on this species has, for the most part, been negative.

The fact that Man has introduced red squirrels to several parts of Canada, and improved their habitat by reforestation, is overshadowed by the number killed each year. Many die from automobiles, guns, and domestic cats, while commercial trapping accounts for several million annually—the catch in Alberta in 1941 was 4,967,933 squirrels.

The American red squirrel has the greatest economic importance of the Canadian Sciuridae. Although the number of pelts has declined during the last two decades, the annual catch still averages three million animals. In addition, these squirrels are a staple food source for larger, and more valuable, furbearers.

On the debit side, they frequently rob birds' nests of eggs and fledglings. Like the other members of the squirrel family, they can also cause damage to cottages and cabins.

From time to time, logging companies mount campaigns to eliminate this species from their timber limits, on the basis that red squirrels cause severe damage to their conifers. This charge is partially correct, but it ignores the fact that these rodents inadvertently plant a great many evergreens, and eat the grubs and boring insects that harm coniferous trees.

Where to Observe

The American red squirrel may be easily observed in towns and cities throughout his range. All you have to do is stroll quietly around his territory—and wait for him to scold you from the branches.

Douglas' Squirrel
Écureuil de Douglas
Tamiasciurus douglasii

Common Names

Because of his close resemblance to the American red squirrel, Douglas' squirrel is often called a western chickaree or western red squirrel. His distinctive underparts have earned him the nicknames yellow belly, and yellow-breasted pine squirrel. Many people know him as the Douglas chickaree.

His scientific name, *Tamiasciurus douglasii*, combines a Latin descriptive phrase with a Latinized surname. *Tamiasciurus* means "the steward who sits in the shadow of his tail", while *douglasii* refers to David Douglas, who classified this species while on an expedition to the Columbia River in 1824. Douglas was a renowned botanist, who is also commemorated in the naming of the Douglas-fir tree.

Description

Douglas' squirrel is the same shape and size as his close relative, the red squirrel (*Tamiasciurus hudsonicus*). Indeed, if he didn't have bright-saffron underparts (an obvious field mark), he could easily be mistaken for a melanistic red squirrel. Like his cousin, he moults twice a year, in the spring and autumn, but his orange eye-ring, black tufted ears, and chestnut tail with light-tipped guard hairs remain constant throughout the year.

In summer his coat is a dark olive-brown with a black flank stripe. His cheeks, feet, and underparts are vivid orange.

In winter his back develops a rufous stripe, his hindquarters turn grey, and the black flank-stripes fade. His feet and underparts show the most noticeable change, turning buff-yellow.

The overall length for this species is approximately 31 cm, and adults of both sexes average 230 g in weight. Albino or melanistic specimens are rare, although a number of hybrid (Douglas/Red) squirrels have been reported.

Douglas' Squirrel

Canadian Range

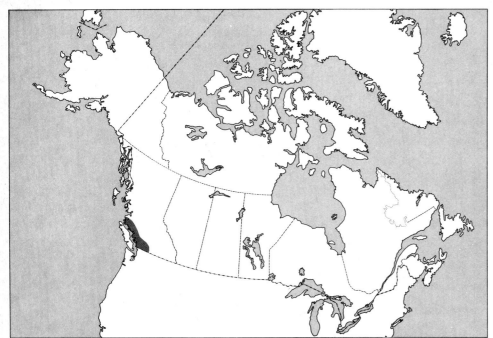

Range

The Canadian range of Douglas'
squirrel is restricted to a narrow strip of
coastal British Columbia that stretches
from the Bella Coola River to the United
States border. His continental range extends as far south as the Sierra Nevada
region of California.

Population density is strongly
influenced by the nourishment value of
the predominant conifer trees. In mixed
stands, the average density is approximately one squirrel per 0.75 ha.

Behaviour

Douglas' squirrel is similar in many ways to the American red squirrel, but there are subtle differences. If anything, Douglas' is even more possessive about his territory. Being a solitary species, each squirrel occupies a specific area whose boundaries are well known to his neighbours. The purpose of the territory is to provide a year-round food supply, and its size is directly related to the number and species of cone-bearing trees it contains. Each day the "owner" makes repeated territorial calls to let everyone know that this is his exclusive property. Should another squirrel enter his domain, these announcements change to threats; if the threats are ignored, a chase ensues. Some intruders are not intimidated by a show of strength, and successfully unseat the resident, but this is the exception rather than the rule. Most interlopers retreat when caught poaching, and when a chase takes place it is usually short and bloodless. Indeed, the territorial instinct is so deeply ingrained that once a trespasser reaches his own property, the roles reverse, and the pursuer becomes the pursued. Usually these encounters are between Douglas' squirrels, but where the species overlap, the intruder may be a red squirrel. The little Townsend's chipmunk can also cause great excitement, for he is the only chipmunk with an inclination to eat hemlock cones, and he is not averse to pinching a free lunch.

The only exception to the boundary rule occurs during the mating season. When a female comes into heat, she allows male squirrels to enter her territory for that particular day. As soon as the suitors gather, one emerges as the dominant animal, and proceeds to chase the others away. The dominant male and the resident female mate following a brief courtship, but by sunset their relationship is over, and he too is no longer welcome.

Douglas' squirrel is highly vocal and seems compelled to comment on everything that catches his eye. Most listeners agree that his voice is more musical than the red squirrel's, although one authority has compared his territorial call to the mechanical sound of a muffled alarm clock, and another described his warning call as an "explosive bark". Like all the squirrels, the more agitated he becomes, the more violently he twitches his tail.

This species has a highly developed system for dealing with seed-bearing cones, which are his main food source. After cutting the cones from several trees in a stand, he returns to the ground and collects them for storage, usually in a shady or damp spot to prevent the cones from drying and shedding their seeds. In prime habitat, the same storage sites are used by successive generations, eventually accumulating a thick layer of debris. Beneath this layer of husks, the vegetation remains moist, and buried cones may be preserved for up to three years. When Douglas' squirrel sets his mind to harvesting he can work with astonishing speed. In California, one animal cut 537 sequoia cones in the space of 30 minutes —an average of one every 3.5 seconds! It should be added that this same squirrel took nearly four days to lug away and cache his booty.

Being diurnal, Douglas' squirrel may be abroad at any time of the day. However, he schedules his active periods to coincide with the most comfortable hours of the season, and usually remains in his nest during inclement weather.

Personality

In 1894, the American naturalist John Muir wrote about Douglas' squirrel in his book *The Mountains of California:* *Though only a few inches long, so intense is his fiery vigor and restlessness, he stirs every grove with wild life, and makes himself more important than even the huge bears that shuffle through the tangled underbrush beneath him. Every wind is fretted by his voice, almost every hole and branch feels the sting of his sharp feet. . . . Seeing a man for the first time, he approaches nearer and nearer, until within a few feet; then, with an angry outburst, he makes a sudden rush, all teeth and eyes, as if about to eat you up. But finding that the big, forked animal doesn't scare, he prudently beats a retreat, and sets himself up to reconnoiter on some overhanging branch, scrutinizing every movement you make with ludicrous solemnity. Gathering courage, he ventures down the trunk again, churring and chirping and jerking nervously up and down in curious loops, eyeing you all the time, as if showing off and demanding your admiration. . . . He is without exception, the wildest animal I ever saw,—a fiery, sputtering little bolt of life, luxuriating in quick oxygen and the woods' best juices. One can hardly think of such a creature being dependent, like the rest of us, on climate and food.*

Habitat

Douglas' squirrel is found from sea level to elevations of approximately 2000 m in dense coniferous forests, logged-over areas, and above timberline. His favourite habitat is a stand of lodgepole pine, Englemann spruce, Douglas fir, or western hemlock.

The size of each animal's territory is determined by the food production of the various trees. A three-year study in the Cascade Mountains of British Columbia revealed that a squirrel living in hemlock stands needs less than 0.50 ha, but one found in lodgepole pine requires nearly 1 ha.

Douglas' squirrel normally occupies a den or nest in a dense coniferous grove, at a height of from 5 to 20 m above ground.

Tree dens are fashioned with an assist from Nature, for they are completed by simply using shredded vegetation to line an existing cavity in a hollow trunk. The two major advantages of this type of dwelling are that it is unobtrusive and is almost completely weatherproof. These benefits make it an ideal winter home or natal den.

Tree nests, or dreys, appear to be flimsy structures, but they are securely attached to the branches or the trunk of the tree, and are often built on the foundation of an abandoned hawk's or crow's nest. From the outside they resemble a ragged ball of vegetation; inside they are snug and warm.

Squirrels living above timberline usually burrow among the loose rocks of a talus.

Feeding Habits

Although most of his diet is the same as that of the red squirrel, the Douglas' is more strictly vegetarian, and he rarely, if ever, robs birds' nests. When he eats animal matter, it is usually in the form of insects or grubs; pregnant or lactating females often gnaw antlers and bones found on the forest floor to boost their calcium intake. Both sexes obtain their liquid requirement from free-standing water, snow, or plants and berries with a high moisture-content.

Their menu changes with the season. In winter, they rely on cones cached the previous autumn and seeds that fall on the snow. In early spring, they eat tree fungi and the bark of several conifers, especially lodgepole pine. With the onset of warm weather, their diet includes the pollen of Douglas fir, lodgepole pine, and Englemann spruce. A few weeks later, they consume fresh greens in the form of birch and alder catkins, as well as a variety of young ferns. Food is plentiful by midsummer, and they can indulge in such delicacies as false truffles, mushrooms, and blueberries. Autumn is a most important period in their calendar, for they must not only look after their immediate food requirements, but also harvest and store sufficient cones to last them through the coming winter.

Life Cycle

This species is polyoestrous, but because of the short summer in the northern part of its range, most British Columbian squirrels bear only one litter each year. Mating takes place in early April, and the young are born 35 days later, around the middle of May. The average litter consists of 4 pups, whose development closely matches that of young red squirrels. The little ones are well looked after by their mother, but soon learn about territorial discipline. Shortly before they are weaned, she moves them from the natal den to a nest close to her territorial boundary, and from then on they are not allowed to enter the main portion of her territory. When they are weaned at 8 weeks, they are on their own. This is a difficult period for the pups because they must learn what foods to eat and how to obtain them. An overriding problem for juvenile squirrels is their lack of a territory, which is the key to a constant food supply. Most attempts to establish a niche in the forest are met with rebuffs, and many juveniles die of starvation during their first winter.

Juveniles that manage to survive the cold months are fully mature the following spring. Because of the high mortality rate of the young, the average life expectancy in the wild of Douglas' squirrel is estimated to be less than 3 years.

This species does not hibernate. However, during periods of heavy precipitation or high wind, the squirrels may remain in their nest for several consecutive days.

Natural Enemies

Douglas' squirrel is preyed upon by the same enemies as the red squirrel. Of the carnivores, the most feared is the pine marten, followed by the fisher, lynx, weasel, mink, and bobcat. The Goshawk and Red-shouldered Hawk are ever-present threats, as are the Sharp-shinned and Sparrow Hawks.

Since these squirrels are primarily residents of the coniferous forest, a cone crop-failure can cause high mortality; and a forest fire can virtually eliminate the resident population.

Relations with Humans

On the positive side, Man has improved the habitat of Douglas' squirrel through reforestation. On the negative side, we have instituted squirrel-control programmes in many of the same areas, and systematically trapped them throughout most of their Canadian range.

The long winter pelt of Douglas' squirrel has commercial value, but owing to the species' limited range, the total number trapped is far less than is the case for the red squirrel. Douglas' squirrel also acts as a food source for larger, more valuable furbearing carnivores. He is not considered a significant agricultural pest, nor does he bear the nest-robbing stigma of his cousins.

The most serious charge against Douglas' squirrels comes from the commercial foresters: that by eating a high percentage of cones in lean years, they slow down the regeneration of the timber limits. To some extent this is true, but the commercial concern is for speed, rather than natural growth of trees. It should also be remembered that squirrels plant countless trees, and even their cone cutting is turned to monetary gain. Each year people raid their caches, collect as many cones as possible, and sell them for seed to forestry services and commercial nurseries. The annual volume of this business amounts to many thousands of litres. In addition, squirrels eat harmful grubs and fungi. A major study in 1969 by Robert B. Finley, Jr., of the U.S. Fish and Wildlife Service, concluded with this sentence:

Nevertheless, a good population of Tamiasciurus *is an invaluable asset wherever man must collect seed for artificial seeding or planting of conifers.*

Where to Observe
Douglas' squirrel can be seen within the city limits of Vancouver, as well as in stands of conifers up and down the coast.

Walk quietly, and listen for his chatter.

Southern Flying Squirrel
Petit polatouche
Glaucomys volans

Common Names

Being the smaller of the two gliding squirrels, he is often called the little flying squirrel. He is also widely known as the eastern flying squirrel because his range is restricted to the eastern half of the continent. The type locality for this species is Virginia, where John Smith, an early settler, wrote in 1624:
A Small beaste they have, they call Assapanick, *but we call them flying Squirrels, because spreading their legs, and so stretching the largenesse of their skins, that they have beene seene to fly 30 or 40 yards.*

His scientific name, *Glaucomys volans*, is most appropriate. *Glaucomys* is Greek meaning "grey mouse", while *volans* is the Latin word for "flying".

Description

From a distance, the southern flying squirrel looks like a large mouse with a bushy tail. At close range, his velvety grey coat is overlaid with tan fur above, and cream-coloured fur below. Along each side of his body is a loose fold of skin that is attached to his wrists and ankles like a cape; the fur on the edge of this membrane is black. He has black shoe-button eyes, prominent ears, and long glistening vibrissae. His tail is covered with silky hairs that grow from the sides like the barbs on a feather.

The southern flying squirrel can be distinguished from the northern flying squirrel by the pale fur on his belly, which is cream coloured to the roots while the underfur of the northern flying squirrel is grey. This test can only be made when the animal is in hand.

This species moults once each year, during September and October. The overall length for adults of both sexes is approximately 24 cm, with their average weight being 65 g.

Southern Flying Squirrel

Canadian Range

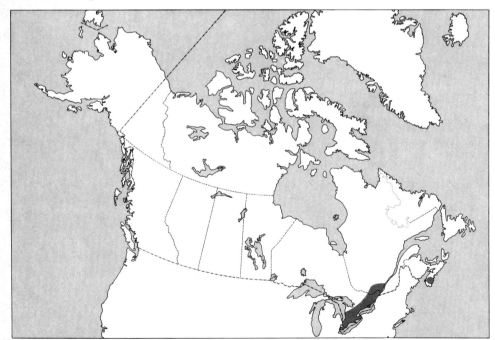

Range

Until the 1950s it was generally believed that the little flying squirrel was restricted to southern Ontario. We now know that the northern extremity of his Canadian range roughly corresponds with a line drawn on the map from Sudbury through Montreal to Halifax. His continental range includes most of the eastern United States, extending as far south as the Gulf of Mexico.

Flying squirrels are much more plentiful than most of us realize, but it is difficult to assess population density because of their nocturnal habits. In suitable terrain, a reasonable estimate is 5 adults to the hectare.

Behaviour

The southern flying squirrel is nocturnal, and more stricly arboreal than the other tree squirrels. His most distinctive characteristic is his ability to glide long distances through the air. He accomplishes this feat by extending his limbs, thus stretching the loose folds of skin along his sides; the increased surface is sufficient to support his weight in the air. All flights are made from a higher level to a lower level, with the angle of descent ranging from 30 to 50 degrees. In some respects, this squirrel's performance is similar to the human sport of "hang-gliding".

Having gauged the distance carefully, he launches himself from the tree with a powerful thrust of his legs and tail; then he spreads his limbs. In flight, he uses his tail as a rudder, and can alter direction by as much as 90 degrees by adjusting the tension on his stretched membranes with movements of his arms and legs. Just before reaching his destination, he drops his lower body and lifts his tail; this combination slows his speed, permitting him to land softly with all four paws. Glides of more than 30 m are made in this manner, although most journeys are considerably shorter. A flying squirrel employs his gliding talent for practical purposes, but he also makes repeated flights seemingly for the sheer joy of it.

When he is high in the trees, or soaring through the air, his folds of loose skin are a distinct asset. On the ground, these membranes have little effect on his mobility, but they may handicap his efforts to swim.

Flying squirrels are gregarious creatures who often feed together, and frequently share the same nest. There is little agonistic behaviour, and the only ones concerned about territory are those with young. Despite her diminutive size, a mother flying squirrel is fearless in protecting her babies. There have been instances where a mother squirrel has made several trips to "rescue" her young that have fallen from the nest and been picked up by humans. Like the other squirrels, she transports her young while they cling to her neck, and she is able to glide expertly when wearing her baby as a ruff.

The southern flying squirrel makes a variety of squeaks and whistles. His most common call is a birdlike *chip*; when he is agitated, this changes to a series of short piping notes.

He has a high standard of personal cleanliness. Should his nest become fouled, he quickly moves to a new home, and he grooms himself carefully each day.

Being nocturnal, he may be active anytime from dusk until dawn, although studies indicate that his most active periods occur around 10 p.m. and again around 3 a.m. On nights with high winds or precipitation, he prefers to stay in his den.

Personality

The January, 1883, issue of *American Naturalist* has an article by F.H. King, in which he tells of some flying squirrels he kept as pets:

I have never known wild animals that became so perfectly familiar and confiding as these young squirrels did; and they seemed to get far more enjoyment from playing upon my person than in any other place, running in and out of pockets, and between my coat and vest. After the frolic was over they always esteemed it a great favor if I would allow them to crawl into my vest in front and go to sleep there, where they felt the warmth of my body, and it was very rare indeed, during the first six months, that they failed to ask the privilege; indeed, they came to consider themselves abused if turned out. When forced to go to sleep by themselves, the attitude taken was amusing, the nose was placed upon the table or other object it happened to be upon, and then it would walk forward over it, rolling itself up until the nose almost protruded from between the hind legs; the tail was then wrapped in a horizontal coil about the feet, and the result was an exquisite little ball of life in soft fur which it seemed almost sacrilegious to touch. If they escaped from the cage during the night, I was sure to be warned of the fact by their coming into the bed to roll themselves up close to my face or neck.

Habitat

The southern flying squirrel makes his home among mature deciduous trees, his favourites being oak, hickory and maple. When these are not present he will choose beech or aspen. Because he requires a great amount of liquids daily, he normally sites his den within 100 m of water. For these reasons, he is often found in neglected woodlots containing a creek or pond.

The average home range for this species is approximately 0.50 ha.

He usually makes his home from 2 to 15 m above ground in a hollow deciduous tree. This tree is always within gliding distance of other trees. Often he occupies a cavity made by a woodpecker, although hollow stumps and holes created by broken branches are also prime sites for interior dens.

Interior dens usually have an entrance hole approximately 5 cm in diameter. Should the entrance be too small, the squirrel gnaws it to the proper size. This type of home is the most popular with the species, and the first choice as a natal den.

Outside nests or dreys are sometimes used in the summer, or as supplementary shelters. These resemble the nests built by grey and fox squirrels, but are more compactly fashioned, with an exterior diameter of approximately 30 cm. The interior of both types of nest is lined with finely shredded vegetation, particularly the inner bark of cedar, and the pile is so deep in winter that the occupants are frequently hidden from sight.

Flying squirrels living close to civilization often make their nests in birdhouses, outbuildings or dwellings. They are so gregarious that as many as a dozen may share the same den, although the average number living together in the summer is 2, while in the winter, because of the need for additional body heat, the average number is 5.

Feeding Habits

The southern flying squirrel has an omniverous appetite, which combined with his insatiable curiosity, leads him to try almost anything. Like the other tree squirrels he eats nuts, seeds, flowers, fruits, mushrooms, and a variety of animal matter including birds' eggs and night-flying insects, such as June bugs and moths. His liquid intake is obtained by drinking water, or by eating fruits and vegetation with a high moisture content.

His favourite staples are nuts and acorns. Most of these are stored in his den, or cached in trees, rather than being buried for the winter. Empty hickory nuts or acorns with a smooth circular opening are a sure sign of his work; the other squirrels break these nuts to pieces, or make a jagged hole.

Life Cycle

Southern flying squirrels are capable of producing two litters annually, the first in April, the second in August. However, because of the short summer in the northern part of their range, most Canadian squirrels bear only a single litter in spring.

Mating takes place in late February and early March. The young are born around the middle of April, after a 40-day gestation period. The average litter consists of 3 pups, each weighing 3.5 g. At birth, the babies are blind and hairless, with a clearly defined flight membrane and webbed paws. By the end of 4 weeks their eyes are open, and they have a fine coat of downy fur. During the next week they begin to explore their surroundings. At this stage, the natal den may have become fouled with scats, or overrun by parasites; in either case their mother will move them to a fresh nest. The little ones taste their first solid food at around 7 weeks, but are not completely weaned until they are 9 weeks old. At 3 months they make their first faltering glides, and by the end of July they are able to fend for themselves. This is just as well, for their mother may have a second litter to contend with in August.

Juveniles usually spend their first winter with their littermates, and separate the following spring to establish their own families. It is normal for 3 to 12 squirrels to share the same tree cavity for the winter. Their den is snugly insulated with shredded vegetation and well-stocked with nuts. This arrangement eliminates the need to leave the nest for food, and preserves maximum body heat.

They do not hibernate in the true sense, but cold weather reduces their activity, and they become quiescent when the temperatures plummet.

The average life-span for this species in the wild is estimated to be around 4 years, although flying squirrels in captivity have lived for up to 13 years.

Natural Enemies

Because this squirrel is nocturnal, he is particularly vulnerable to attack from owls. In addition, he is preyed upon by a number of carnivores including martens, mink, weasels, and raccoons.

Near urban areas, his worst enemy is the domestic cat.

Relations with Humans

As we have cleared the land, we have steadily reduced the natural habitat for this species. Where trees are grown commercially, in woodlots for example, it is sound forestry practice to cull out those that are old or dead. These trees are the principal nesting sites for the southern flying squirrel.

He has no direct economic value because his pelt lacks durability. However, he is commercially valuable in an indirect way because he eats harmful grubs and insects, and is a food source for furbearing carnivores.

These squirrels are harmless, except for being a minor nuisance should they take up residence in an occupied dwelling. They make gentle and charming pets, but it is well to remember that they are nocturnal, and must be allowed to sleep during the day.

Where to Observe

The southern flying squirrel is common to many areas but because of his nocturnal habits he is rarely seen. A farmer's woodlot is a good place to look for him; any mature oak, hickory, or maple tree with a woodpecker's hole is a likely home. You can knock on the tree with a stick, or return at dusk and listen for his chirping call. If it is a moonlit night you may see his silhouette as he glides overhead.

Northern Flying Squirrel
Grand polatouche
Glaucomys sabrinus

Common Names
He is often called the big flying
squirrel or the Canadian flying squirrel.
Both names are appropriate, because he
is almost twice the size of the southern
flying squirrel, and his range encom-
passes most of Canada.

His scientific name, *Glaucomys
sabrinus*, was given to him in 1801 by a
zoologist named George Shaw but it took
nearly one hundred years for it to be
generally accepted. *Glaucomys* is Greek
meaning "grey mouse"; *sabrinus* is Latin
meaning "river nymph", and refers to
the Severn River on the west coast of
Hudson Bay, the locality where this
species was first identified.

Description
Northern and southern flying squirrels are similar in appearance, except that
the northern is much bigger, and might
easily be mistaken for a red squirrel in a
floppy grey overcoat.

Like his smaller cousin, he has
luminous black eyes, rounded ears, and
long vibrissae. His head and upper body
are various shades of grey, washed with
beige along his back and hindquarters.
The fur on the edge of his flight membranes is almost black, which contrasts
with the light buff of his underparts. His
tail is smoke-grey above, and pale below.

One way to identify this species is to
look closely at the fur on his belly—the
hairs on the northern flying squirrel are
lead-coloured at the base, while those of
the southern are pale to their roots.

Northern flying squirrels moult once
each year, in autumn. The overall length
for adults of both sexes is approximately
31 cm and their average weight is 160 g.

Northern Flying Squirrel

Canadian Range

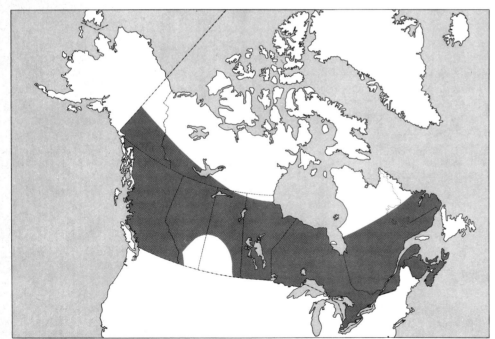

Range

The northern flying squirrel has a gigantic range, which stretches in a broad band across Canada, extending north to Alaska on the Pacific coast, and into Labrador on the Atlantic coast. He is not found in southeastern Alberta, southwestern Saskatchewan, or on the islands of Anticosti and Newfoundland. His continental range includes portions of the American northwest and northeast.

The number of squirrels in a given area depends upon the terrain. In suitable habitat, the population density may be as high as a pair for every 2 ha, but most regions are more sparsely settled.

Behaviour

The northern flying squirrel is strictly nocturnal, spending most of his time in trees. Like the southern, he is graceful and agile above ground, and he is also quite nimble on land because his elastic flight membranes are retractable. Both species could more accurately be called "gliding", rather than "flying" squirrels, because they do not fly— rather, they glide from a higher level down to a lower level.

In practice, by extending his limbs, the capelike fur on his sides becomes taut, giving him a flat rectangular shape, similar to that of a kite. This resemblance is heightened by the fact that his tail acts as a stabilizer, like the tail of a kite (although in the squirrel's case, it also serves as a rudder). He invariably launches himself for flight from a head-down position. In the air, he can change course several times if necessary by adjusting the tension on his lateral folds, or by manipulating his tail. Landings are made with his head up, by lifting his tail and using his cape as an air brake. This series of manoeuvres reduces his speed almost to stalling point, and allows him to alight softly. Upon landing he will sometimes scurry to the other side of the tree, and flick his tail in such a way that he appears to have gone in the opposite direction. This is probably an instinctive precautionary measure against predators.

The northern flying squirrel is scrupulously clean and spends part of each day engaged in a grooming ritual.

First he washes his paws and forearms with his tongue, then he cleans his head and neck with his paws. His body fur is both licked with his tongue and combed with his paws. His silky tail is held by its tip, and combed with his teeth.

The typical call of the northern flying squirrel is a metallic *chuck chuck*, which is similar to that of the other tree squirrels. If he is annoyed or upset, these sounds change to a squeaky falsetto. When he is relaxed, he sometimes utters melodious chirping notes like those of a bird.

These squirrels have a very happy relationship with each other. Not only do they often share nests, but the mate of a female with a litter will usually stay nearby so he can be with her when she isn't looking after her babies. They are also sociable with humans. J. Dewey Soper, a pioneer Canadian conservationist and naturalist, wrote in *The Mammals of Alberta:*
In disposition, flying squirrels are mild and gentle. As pets they are sweet-tempered, docile little creatures and bear repeated handling without sign of resentment.

Personality

Cy Hampson, of Edmonton, has studied the behaviour of the northern flying squirrel, and has kept many as pets. In a recent letter, he wrote:
Would you know more of the boundless enthusiasm and trusting nature of these incomparable gliders of the night? Closet half a hundred of them in spacious laboratory and tend them there. When paying them a visit, squeeze swiftly through the door and close it quickly behind you. On the instant you are deluged with flying squirrels, converging from all directions. Sailing in from tall nesting stumps, lamp cords and window sills. Scampering across the floor from feeding trays and distant corners. Landing on your shoulders, your chest, your back, your head. Rushing up your legs and arms. Eagerly exploring your pant cuffs, your trouser legs, sleeves, pockets and the inside of your shirt. Hunting for tidbits—sunflower seeds, raisins, nuts, rose hips, flakes of oatmeal. Then seeking out places to hide these delectable treasures.

An hour later, it is utterly impossible to retire gracefully. Only with the quickest of eye and nimblest of footwork can you make your getaway without bearing half a dozen of your delightful charges, clinging tenaciously to various parts of your person.

Habitat

The northern flying squirrel lives among coniferous trees, or stands containing conifers, at altitudes from sea level to 2000 m. Typical western habitat is an open forest of spruce and cedar. In the east, he is often found in mixed stands of birch and hemlock.

The home range for this species varies with the terrain and tree density; most squirrels occupy an area of approximately 2 ha.

The northern flying squirrel likes to live among coniferous trees, and he normally sites his home from 1 to 10 m above ground. Two types of dwellings are used: interior dens, and exterior nests or dreys.

Most interior dens are made for him by woodpeckers, who originally excavated the cavity for their own home; or by natural deterioration of the wood, which creates a hollow in the trunk. When a flying squirrel moves in, he will line the cavity with finely shredded vegetation.

Outside dreys look like fibrous balls of moss and lichen, and may easily be mistaken for the nest of a red squirrel, Blue Jay, or Magpie. This is an understandable error, because the northern flying squirrel often refurbishes the vacant premises of these three species, rather than building his own home from "scratch".

Interior dens are preferred for winter living and the bearing of young, while outside nests are more popular for summer residence. During the course of a year, the same squirrel may occupy several different homes, and many females who give birth in a den cavity subsequently move their young to an outside nest.

Feeding Habits

The diet of the northern flying squirrel is similar to that of other tree squirrels. Like his southern cousin, he needs water on a regular basis, and his wide-ranging tastes include animal matter in the form of insects, carrion, and occasionally, birds' eggs.

During summer he eats seeds, flowers, fruits, fungi, and lichens. In autumn, he concentrates on coniferous seeds and mushrooms, many of which are cached in his den or in nearby trees. With the onset of winter, he is forced to rely on his stores and the bark of various conifers. In spring, he feasts on the buds of aspen, alder, and pussy willow.

Ernest Thompson Seton observed in *Lives of Game Animals* that the northern flying squirrel had a sweet tooth that often proved his undoing, as many were drowned in sap buckets. A half century later, an article in *Canadian Audubon* mentioned a man who spent the winter of 1962 on a wooded island and had a northern flying squirrel visitor who would drink apple juice from the can.

The squirrels' appetite for meat is another source of trouble because they are frequently caught while trying to eat the bait in marten traps.

Life Cycle

Throughout most of their range, northern flying squirrels mate at the end of March and the beginning of April. The young are born during May, with the average litter consisting of 3 deaf, blind, and hairless pups, each weighing approximately 6 g.

By the time the little ones are a month old they have quadrupled their birth weight, and short dark fur covers both their bodies and their tails, which are round rather than flat. During their fifth week they open their eyes. Their coordination and appearance continue to improve in the ensuing days; by the sixth week the hairs on their tail grow from the sides like those of an adult. They are weaned around their ninth week. At this stage, they become increasingly independent; by the end of the third month they are attempting to glide. At four months, they are proficient gliders, and able to take care of themselves without the help of their mother. Some leave the nest permanently, but many choose to share a den with their mother for their first winter. Northern flying squirrels do not hibernate, but remain active during the most bitter sub-zero weather. One trait that helps them cope with the winter is their habit of sharing the same den. Up to a dozen may congregate in a well-insulated nest, which gives them both companionship and a generous amount of body heat.

Young of the year are fully mature by the following spring. The average life-span for this species in the wild is estimated to be from 3 to 4 years, although northern flying squirrels have lived up to 10 years in captivity.

Natural Enemies

The predators of the northern flying squirrel are basically the same as those that prey upon the southern flying squirrel. On land, his main enemies are the marten, lynx, bobcat, ermine, and fisher. Being nocturnal, flying squirrels are rarely taken by hawks, but they are a staple item in the diet of owls, particularly that of the Great Horned Owl.

Few of these raptorial species are present near civilization, but the domestic cat, who hunts both day and night, more than compensates for their absence.

Relations with Humans

Man has made no deliberate effort to harm this species, but the encroachment of civilization has gradually reduced the habitat of the northern flying squirrel.

He has no direct economic value because his pelt is too fragile for commercial use. Trappers in the North regard flying squirrels as pests because they frequently spring the traps set for large carnivores. On the other hand, this species acts as a food source for some valuable furbearers.

The northern flying squirrel is harmless to the agricultural community. The worst that can be said of him is that he is a nuisance when he occupies a birdhouse, or the attic of a home. In discussing these trivial misdemeanors, the noted American naturalist, Arthur H. Howell, said:

. . . ordinarily their gentle and confiding ways and their interesting habits make them desirable neighbours.

Where to Observe

Keep in mind that the northern flying squirrel sleeps during the day, and is only active after dark. Study the trees in suitable habitat carefully, and once you have located a nest return to the spot on a still moonlit night. If he is in residence, you will probably hear him, and possibly see him sail across the sky.

Aestivate
To pass the summer in a state of torpor.

Agonistic
Aggressive or defensive behaviour, such as fighting between individuals usually of the same species.

Albino
An animal with an abnormal lack of pigment in its colouring, causing the hair to be white, and the eyes to be pink and unduly sensitive to light.

Anorexia
Prolonged loss of appetite.

Botfly
A parasitic insect that lays its eggs on animals; the eggs develop into larvae that lodge beneath the skin of the host animal.

Buckbrush
A shrubby plant that furnishes browse for various animals. It is sometimes also called wolfberry or coralberry.

Canine Teeth
Any of the four pointed teeth between the incisors and molars. Sometimes called eyeteeth in mammals.

Carnivore
A member of the mammalian order Carnivora; also any animal that feeds on other animals.

Conifer
A cone-bearing evergreen tree, such as spruce, pine, and cedar.

Corm
The fleshy underground stem that produces a plant such as a crocus, gladiolus, or tuberous begonia.

Deciduous Tree
In Canada, a tree whose leaves shed in autumn. Examples include maple, elm, and poplar trees.

Dentition
The kind, number, and arrangement of teeth.

Diastema
The gap between the incisors and rear molars in a rodent's arrangement of teeth.

Diurnal
Active during the daylight hours.

Drey
A squirrel's nest of leaves and twigs.

Erythrism
A condition marked by excessive redness in the hair of animals (adj. erythristic).

Forbs
Broad-leaved herbs other than grass.

Fungi
A group of plants without stems, leaves, or roots, which reproduce by spores. Examples include mushrooms, puffballs, and molds.

Germinate
In plants, to sprout or bud.

Hardpan
A cemented or compacted, often clayey layer under soft soil that is impenetrable by roots.

Herbivore
An animal that feeds on plants.

Glossary

Hibernaculum
A shelter occupied during winter by a dormant animal.

Hibernation
The time spent in a torpid or dormant state during winter.

Home Range
The area to which the activities of an animal are confined.

Incisors
The front or cutting teeth, located between the canine teeth on the premaxillary bone of the skull.

Interaction
The action or reciprocal behaviour between one animal and another.

Larva (pl. larvae)
The early developmental stage of advanced insects that have hatched from eggs. Examples are maggots, grubs, and caterpillars.

Lichen
Cellular plants without a stem or leaves, consisting of algae and fungi, which grow on trees and rocks.

Mammal
Any of a class of vertebrate animals comprising Man and all other animals that nourish their young with milk secreted by mammary glands, and that are usually more or less covered with hair.

Mammalogist
One who studies mammals.

Mandible
The lower jaw consisting of a single bone or of completely fused bones.

Masseter
A large muscle that activates the lower jaw and assists in chewing.

Matriarchy
A society marked by the recognized supremacy of the mother (adj. matriarchal).

Melanism
Abnormal dark pigment in the skin and hair of mammals. Black-coloured grey squirrels are an example (adj. melanistic)

Metabolism
The physical and chemical processes by which a mammal converts materials into living tissue, energy, and waste.

Midden
A tree squirrel's refuse heap, created over time by feeding adjacent to its storehouse of food.

Monoestrous
Having a single breeding period each year.

Natal
Pertaining to birth.

Nocturnal
Done in or pertaining to the hours of darkness.

Ochreous
A brownish-yellow or rusty-yellow colour.

Olfactory
Pertaining to the sense of smell.

Omnivore
One that feeds on both animal and vegetable matter.

Parasite
An animal or insect that lives in or on an another animal, and takes nourishment from that animal, usually to the detriment of the host organism.

Patriarchy
A society dominated by older and stronger males (adj. patriarchal).

Pelage
The hair or fur covering the body of a mammal.

Permafrost
A permanently frozen layer of subsoil occurring in frigid regions.

Plantigrade
An animal that walks on the whole sole of its foot, rather than on the toes only. Bears and Man are typical plantigrades.

Polygamy
Having more than one mate (adj. polygamous).

Polyoestrous
Having more than one breeding period in a year.

Premaxilla
A bone, bearing the incisors, that forms front of the upper jaw in vertebrates.

Raptor
A predatory bird that preys on weaker species.

Reforestation
The renewal of forest cover by seeding or planting.

Rocky Mountain Spotted Fever
A disease caused by *Rickettsia* transmitted by ticks, resulting in high fever, pains, and a rash; it is often fatal.

Rodentia
An order of gnawing animals that includes squirrels, rats, mice, beavers, and porcupines, among others.

Rufous
Reddish-brown colour.

Samara
Winged, seed-bearing fruit, produced by certain deciduous trees, including the maple, ash, and elm.

Sciuridae
The squirrel family, all of whom are members of the order Rodentia.

Swale
A low-lying or depressed and often wet stretch of land.

Talus
A sloping mass of rock fragments, usually at the base of a cliff or mountain.

Territory
That part of an animal's home range that is defended against intruders of the same species.

Torpor
The state of being dormant or inactive.

Tree-line
The upper limit of growth in mountains or high latitudes. Also called Timberline.

Vegetarian
One who feeds solely on plant and vegetable matter.

Vibrissae
The whiskers or long stiff hairs about the mouth of an animal; they frequently serve as organs of touch.

Witches'-Broom
An abnormal tufted growth of small branches on a tree or shrub caused by fungi or viruses. Also called Staghead.

Zoology
A branch of biology dealing with animals, including their classification, physiology, and habits.

Zoologist
One who studies zoology.

Zygomatic Arch
A bony arch on each side of the skull of vertebrates, joining the cranial and facial bones, consisting of the cheekbone and its connections.

Banfield, A.W.F.
(1974). The mammals of Canada.
University of Toronto Press.

Bernard, R.
(1940). Occurrence of *Citellus tridecemlineatus* in the province of Quebec. Le naturaliste canadien 67(2):155–56.

Brand, L.R.
(1974). Tree nests of California chipmunks (Eutamias). American Midland Naturalist 91(2):489–91.

Broadbooks, H.E.
(1958). Life history and ecology of the chipmunk, *Eutamias amoenus*, in eastern Washington. University of Michigan, Museum of Zoology, Miscellaneous Publication 103:1–42.

Bruemmer, Fred
(1972). Encounters with Arctic animals. Toronto: McGraw-Hill Ryerson.

Cowan, I. McTaggart, and C.J. Guiguet
(1966). The mammals of British Columbia. British Columbia Provincial Museum Handbook 11.

Criddle, Stuart
(1939). The thirteen-striped ground squirrel in Manitoba. Canadian Field-Naturalist 53(1):1–6.

Finley, R.B., Jr.
(1969). Cone caches and middens of Tamiasciurus in the Rocky Mountain region. University of Kansas, Museum of Natural History Miscellaneous Publication 51:233–73.

Godfrey, W.E.
(1966). The birds of Canada. Ottawa: National Museums of Canada.

Gordon, Kenneth
(1943). The natural history and behavior of the western chipmunk and the mantled ground squirrel. Oregon State College Monographs, Studies in Zoology 5:1–104.

Hollister, N.
(1916). A systematic account of the prairie-dogs. North American Fauna 40:1–36.

King, F.H.
(1883). Instinct and memory exhibited by the flying squirrel in confinement, with a thought on the origin of wings in bats. American Naturalist 17(1):36–42.

Klugh, A.B.
(1923). Notes on the habits of the chipmunk *Tamias striatus* (Lystery). Journal of Mammalogy 4(1): 29–32.

Lloyd, Hoyes
(1925). The acclimatization of the fox squirrel at Pelee Island, Ontario, Canada. Canadian Field-Naturalist 39(6):138.

MacClintock, Dorcas
(1970). Squirrels of North America. Toronto: Van Nostrand Reinhold.

Mathews, R.K.
(1971). Wilds animals as pets. Garden City, N.Y.: Doubleday.

Melchior, H.R.
(1971). Characteristics of Arctic ground squirrel alarm calls. Oecologia 7(2):184–90.

Merriam, C.H.
(1884). The mammals of the Adirondack region, northeastern New York. New York: the author.

Michener, D.R.
(1974). Annual cycle of activity and weight changes in Richardson's ground squirrel (*Spermophilus richardsonii*). Canadian Field-Naturalist 88(4):409–14.

Michener, G.R.
(1977). The effect of climatic conditions on the annual activity and hibernation cycle of Richardson's ground squirrels and Columbian ground squirrels. Canadian Journal of Zoology 55(4):693–703.

Muir, John
(1894). The mountains of California. New York: Century.

Nee, J.A.
(1969). Reproduction in a population of yellow-bellied marmots (*Marmota flaviventris*). Journal of Mammalogy 50(4):756–65.

Pittman, H.H.
(1955). The gophers of the prairie. Canadian Geographical Journal 51(5):198–205.

Saunders, L.G.
(1965). Habits of Franklin's ground squirrel, *Citellus franklini*. Victoria Naturalist 22:55–57.

Seton, E.T.
(1909). Life-histories of Northern animals. Vol I—Grass-eaters. New York: Charles Scribner's Sons.
(1929). Lives of Game Animals. Vol. IV, pt. 1, Rodents, etc. Garden City, N.Y.: Doubleday, Doran and Company.

Soper J.D.
(1961). The mammals of Manitoba. Canadian Field-Naturalist 75(4):171–219. Reprinted, with index, as Canadian Wildlife Management Bulletin, series 1, no. 7.
(1964). The mammals of Alberta. Edmonton: Hamly Press.

Wagner, Jeannie
(1972). The prairie dogs of Val Marie. Nature Canada 1(1):12–17.

Bibliography

Metric Conversion

1 centimetre	0.39	inch
1 metre	39.37	inches
1 hectare	2.47	acres
1 kilometre	0.62	mile
1 gram	0.035	ounce
1 kilogram	2.2046	pounds
0° Celsius	32°	Fahrenheit

Index